THE INCREDIBLE DEBORAH

THE INCREDIBLE DEBORAH
A Story Based on the Life of Deborah Sampson

BY CORA CHENEY

CHARLES SCRIBNER'S SONS
NEW YORK

I wish particularly to thank Mr. Donald Gibbs of the Redwood Library in Newport, Rhode Island; Mrs. Edmund Wordell of the Newport (Rhode Island) Historical Society; Miss Marion Conant of the Dedham (Massachusetts) Historical Society; Mrs. Leah K. Rockwell of the Middleborough (Massachusetts) Public Library; and the many staff members of the numerous New England public libraries and societies where the historical detective work took place.

For two people I love,
Isabel and Henry Eccles

THE INCREDIBLE DEBORAH

December 17, 1760: *Born to Jonathan Sampson, Junior, and his wife Deborah Bradford Sampson, a girl, Deborah, at Plympton in the County of Plymouth, in the Colony of Massachusetts in America.*

I

1765: The British Parliament passed the Stamp Act.

It was warm and soft in the trundle bed. Hannah leaned over her.

"Get up, Deborah," Hannah said. "Put on your outer garments."

Deborah gave her eight-year-old sister a sleepy scowl and kept her eyes tightly shut. It was fun to tease Hannah.

"Get up, if you please," pleaded Hannah. "Grand-mère says to. Jonny has gone for the granny woman, and I'm to take you and Eph to Cousin Fuller for the day."

"Grandmère!" Deborah kicked the covers off and leaped to the cold floor. She ran to the fire where the old woman sat erectly, still in her cloak, holding her head high in the French manner. Deborah scrambled onto her grandmother's lap.

"When did you come?" she asked, hugging Grandmother Bradford.

"Just now, in a farmer's cart from Plymouth," said Grandmère. "And just in time, I'd say."

Deborah glanced over her grandmother's shoulder at her mother, who lay in bed. Mother was acting strangely lately, but everything would be fine now that Grandmère was here.

"Tell me the story about Joan and the soldiers," demanded Deborah. Grandmère was French. Bathsheba La Broche had been her name before she married Elisha Bradford.

"Not now. This is no time for tales of the Maid of Orleans," said Grandmère. "Get on your clothes. You and Hannah and Ephraim are to go to your Cousin Fuller's for a special reason. Scat now."

Deborah stiffened. "Why am I going? I don't want to," she said defiantly, looking at Grandmère.

Hannah, standing anxiously by her mother, held her breath. That Deborah, she would speak out to anyone. But Grandmère only laughed and stood up, dumping Deborah into a heap on the floor, where she landed atop the screeching cat.

"Who asked if you want to, miss? Get on with

2

you. My feet are warm now, and I have no more time for you today. But leave your mother be. You're past four years old now, and big enough to be some help."

She looked over her tiny spectacles at the little girl who sat on the floor with her bottom lip poked out. People said little Deborah had the spirit of the old lady and that Grandmère spoiled her because she admired spunky children.

Deborah pulled on her shoes and put her dress on over her linen petticoat. She helped herself to a tankard of milk and some bread from the table. Her brothers, Elisha and Ephraim, were bringing in armloads of wood and silently stacking it by the hearth. They weren't scuffling and dragging their feet as usual. All the while Mother continued to lie in bed, her face turned to the wall, the curtain half pulled. The air was uneasy with mysterious, half-spoken things.

Grandmère took off her cloak and moved stiffly about the room, making ready for something. She filled the kettles with water and hung them over the fire and then hovered over Mother for a moment.

"Hurry up, child," said Grandmère briskly.

Deborah tried to swallow the milk over the lump in her throat. What had Hannah meant when she said that Brother Jonny had gone to fetch the granny woman? Was the granny woman a witch? She wore a long black cape and carried a satchel. Deborah crept over to Mother. Perhaps she could hide under the covers beside her, and Mother would tell her about rainbows and flowers as

3

she sometimes did. A little moan came from her mother.

"Deborah, don't bother your mother," said Grand-mère sharply, turning from the fire.

Suddenly Deborah began to wail. "I want my mother. I want my father," she cried, sobbing convulsively. "I want to hear about the Maid of Orleans!" She hurled herself onto the floor. "I don't like the granny woman."

"There, there," said Hannah gently. "Don't cry. The granny woman is going to help Mother born the new baby."

But Deborah lay on the floor kicking and screaming until Eph poured a gourd of water from the leather bucket into his little sister's face.

Deborah stopped wailing instantly and jumped up to chase Eph out of the house into the April morning.

"Oh, that vixen," said Grandmère, shaking her head. "What's to become of her? Here, Hannah, take the hornbook and go with them to your Cousin Fuller's. Deborah can amuse herself learning more letters today. I'll send Jonny or Elisha to fetch you when the baby is born."

The cool morning wind turned the wet spot on Deborah's sleeve into a chilly patch as she darted up the road after Eph. Hannah, like a miniature mother, hurried along behind carrying the hornbook and a shawl for Deborah.

"I'll get you, Eph," shouted Deborah, pausing just long enough to pick up a rock and hurl it at him. But six-

Copy of a postcard of the house in Plympton, Massachusetts where it is believed Deborah was born.

year-old Eph had disappeared behind a tree and stood there laughing, tripping Deborah as she ran past.

They fell into a laughing, wrestling, mass on the damp road.

Hannah leaned over them with prim authority. She grabbed Deborah by the shoulder, pulled her to her feet, and shook her.

"Look at you, Deborah, all wet and dirty, fighting on the public road like a, well, not like a *Bradford*," fumed Hannah. She dusted Deborah's dress and wrapped the shawl snugly around her.

"And you too, Eph," called Hannah to the little

boy who was trudging ahead, dusting off his own breeches.

"Oh, pooh, Hannah," said Deborah. "I'm not a Bradford. I'm Deborah Sampson." But she walked meekly beside Hannah, holding her hand quietly for a change. She knew how Mother felt about behaving like a Bradford. Poor Mother. She would be good all day, just for her.

"But you are a Bradford," said Hannah. "Mother was a Bradford before she married Father. Our great-great-grandfather was Governor William Bradford of the Plymouth Colony.

"I know," said Deborah. "Don't you think I know anything? Mother tells me all the time. And so were Miles Standish and John Alden and Peter Hobart and Abraham Sampson our ancestors."

"You do catch on very fast," said Hannah. "I don't believe I could remember all those names myself."

"Most likely not," said Deborah matter-of-factly. "And I know my letters better than Eph does."

"Pride goeth before a fall," admonished Hannah.

"Why?" asked Deborah.

"Oh, stop asking *why*. Just because it does. That's why," said Hannah.

"Hannah," said Deborah, hanging back a moment as they approached Cousin Fuller's yard. "Is Father ever coming back?"

"I—I hope so," said Hannah. "He came back from the sea before, didn't he?"

"But Mother cried. She said her baby would be fatherless. Hannah, will the granny woman bring the baby in her satchel?" Deborah looked questioningly at Hannah.

"I don't know," said Hannah. "Cousin Fuller is beckoning. Eph must have told her we are on our way."

Deborah broke away, her mood changing like the April clouds overhead.

"Cousin Fuller, I can say all my letters now," shouted Deborah as she ran up the walk to the tidy house where Mistress Fuller lived with her brother. "I have come to say them to you."

"Make your manners first, children," said Mistress Fuller.

Hannah, Ephraim, and Deborah drew up in a formal line in front of their cousin. Deborah and Hannah curtsied, Ephraim bowed.

"Good morning, Cousin," they said in unison.

Cousin Fuller smiled down over her plump cheeks and pulled three round molasses cookies from her apron pocket. Deborah smiled back, forgetting her problems of the morning. Cousin Fuller was as round and soft and comforting as a fresh-baked loaf and as sweet as the cookies she always produced from her white linen pocket.

What a wonderful day, first to see Grandmère, and then to chase Eph, and then to visit at Cousin Fuller's. It would have been good to stay home with Grandmère, and her stories. But of course Grandmère was in no mood for her today because the granny woman was coming with her magic satchel of babies.

What would the baby be like, she wondered as she sat in the sun on the kitchen steps munching her cooky. Perhaps she could put the baby beside her in the trundle bed, like a doll. Or she could carry it about on her back like the papooses that the Indian women brought into Plymouth on market days.

"Oh, I shall love my baby," said Deborah sunnily to Cousin Fuller.

"Of course," agreed her cousin.

"She won't need a father. I'll be her father," announced Deborah.

"Don't be pert. Your own father will be home soon, I'll warrant. Come, show me how you read your letters," said Cousin Fuller.

Hannah pulled her sampler from her pocket and began making neat cross-stitches. Deborah leaned over her sister's shoulder and read aloud.

> "Hannah Sampson is my name
> Great Britain is my nation
> Plympton is my dwelling place
> And Christ is my salvation."

"You knew it by heart," said Eph scornfully.

Cousin Fuller sat down in the sun beside them, and holding the little horn-covered card in her hand she passed it first to Eph and then to Deborah.

Eph read off the alphabet printed across the top, but Deborah put her hands over her eyes and recited her letters by heart.

"Very good," said Cousin Fuller, glancing down at

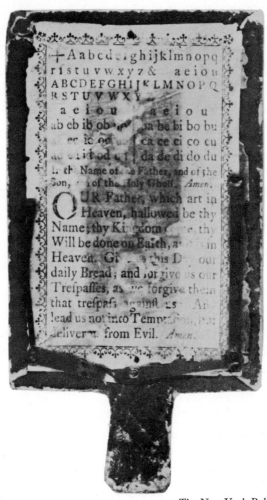

A typical hornbook.

9

Deborah in surprise. "When I taught dame school my older pupils did no better."

Deborah picked up the hornbook and proudly began to read aloud the letters and words on the card. "In the name of the Father and the Son and the Holy Ghost," she finished, tossing a gloating glance at Eph, who kicked her ankle.

"My, I think you're ready for a New England primer," said Cousin Fuller. "But come along, you and Eph are going to work on the tape looms while I teach Hannah to set the piece for a woven bedspread."

"Why can't I do that too?" asked Deborah. "I hate weaving tapes." She fastened her steel-blue eyes on her cousin.

Cousin Fuller gave Deborah a smack on the seat of her linsey-woolsey skirt and turned to Hannah.

Deborah and Eph wove tapes on the frames while Deborah sang, making up little verses about the baby. How handy the tapes would be for the diapers. She had finished six inches of tape and had eaten her dinner of cold venison and bread and cheese when Jonny and Elisha came into the yard.

"The granny woman and Grandmère said to tell you—" shouted Elisha.

"Shut up, Elisha, I'll tell the news," panted Jonny with the importance of a twelve-year-old boy putting his ten-year-old brother in his place. "Grandmère said to tell you that Mother is safely delivered of a fine boy. They will name him after Uncle Nehemiah."

"And, Deborah," the snubbed Elisha whispered

spitefully, "do you know what the granny woman said? She said 'My, what a fine boy. Now that you have him you can put that youngest girl on the shelf.' That means you, Deborah. You aren't the baby at our house any more."

Deborah and Eph spent the night in Cousin Fuller's feather bed while Hannah went home to help. Eph was soon asleep, but Deborah lay rigid in the billowy bed, her lips tight and her heart cold and afraid.

"Laid on the shelf," Elisha had said. What did it mean? Was it a punishment for being a girl? Would she be wrapped in cheesecloth and stuffed on the shelf like an old cheese for the mice to nibble and the flies to sting? Would that wretched boy baby Nehemiah be snug in her own trundle bed while she slept on the shelf? Hot tears filled her eyes. She sniffed.

"Bless me, what's the matter with the little thing?" said Mistress Fuller to her brother, who was mending a harness by the firelight. She bustled over to the bed. "What is it, child?"

But Deborah could neither answer nor stop crying. How could she explain? She looked past Cousin Fuller's shoulder and began to wail.

"It's because I see a witch over there on the shelf," she cried.

"Silly goose," replied Cousin Fuller, looking behind her at the neat kitchen shelf. "That's not a witch. That's only a pitcher of yeast with a cloth tied over the top. Now go to sleep, and I'll make you raised griddlecakes from it for your breakfast. Say your prayers again. That dispels witches."

Deborah woke with the sun streaming in on the floor through the glass window. Remembering her promise of the night before Cousin Fuller was pouring batter onto the griddle over the fire.

"Wash and dress," commanded her cousin. Eph was already at the well splashing water on his face and brushing his teeth with a hickory toothbrush. The day was bonny, and the cakes were light as goose down. Deborah had scarcely finished her first one when Jonny appeared at the door.

"Mother says to fetch you two home now," he said, flopping down on the bench and accepting Cousin Fuller's invitation to eat. "What a racket we have at our house," he said, mumbling because his mouth was full. "Elisha and I bedded in the loft, and with Grandmère and the granny woman creaking about all night and the baby bleating like a newborn lamb, you could hardly say we slept. They didn't care if we slept or ate either. Elisha and I would have starved if Hannah hadn't given the baby to Mother to nurse and mixed us some white-pot."

"Hannah was holding the baby?" asked Deborah, putting down her spoon.

"Sure. Hannah is going to be its little mother, Grandmère said. And she can have it for all I care."

"Me too," said Eph stoutly, swinging his shoulders back in imitation of his brother.

Deborah felt the griddlecakes grow into a knot in her throat. So Hannah was going to give all her attention to the new baby. She pushed back her plate. She didn't want to eat or see the new baby either. She might run away and live with the Indians. But God would surely punish her, she decided miserably, if she didn't obey Mother and come home.

She ran down the road, her heart beating fast. Much as she hated the thought of the new baby, fearful as she was of the mysterious place she would have on the shelf, her curiosity won out. She must rush on to meet her new rival who was now the center of the household.

Deborah opened the kitchen door and crept into the dark interior. The fire was glowing, and Grandmère sat by the hearth rocking back and forth in the maple rocker, crooning a lullaby in French to a squalling bundle of linen in her lap. Mother was in bed, her back turned to the room, and Hannah was quietly washing the dishes. The granny woman was nowhere about.

"Do you want to see your little brother?" asked Grandmère.

Deborah didn't answer. She kept her mouth in a firm straight line. She stared in distaste at the ugly red thing in Grandmère's lap. The baby quieted, and Grandmère motioned to Hannah, who laid it in the low cradle by the fire. Grandmère beckoned to Deborah to climb into the warm spot on her lap.

"Deborah Sampson," said Grandmère, keeping her voice low so she wouldn't waken Mother, "when I was a

13

little girl I learned a verse with a lesson I have never forgotten."

"What verse?" Grandmère always had something interesting to tell.

"First go quietly to the window and tell me what you see," said Grandmère.

Deborah ran to the window. "I see leaves coming out on the trees, and I see bloodroot in the yard, and I see white clouds and blue sky, and a farmer's cart, and an old dog."

"Did you see yourself?" asked Grandmère.

"How could I see myself?" asked Deborah, puzzled.

"So you forgot about yourself, didn't you, miss? You forgot all about your hurt feelings." She tickled Deborah in the ribs, making her laugh aloud when she answered yes.

"This is the way the poem goes," said Grandmère. "Say it after me.

> When I look out the window I can see
> Things that make me forget about me."

Deborah repeated it. "I see what it means. It helps me forget about bad things when I forget about myself and think of something else. I won't forget that, Grandmère."

"See that you don't," said the old lady.

"Now tell me about Joan of Arc and how Harvard College burned down and all the wonderful happenings in Boston town," begged Deborah.

Grandmère chuckled. "Oh, Deborah, who will ever

be able to fill that busy mind of yours? Very well, I shall tell you about the Maid of Orleans. She was a poor girl who went to the King and said she wanted soldiers so she could lead the French Army into battle against the British."

"Did the King give her the army?" asked Deborah, knowing what the answer would be.

"Oh, yes. After many troubles the King of France finally gave Joan an army, and she fought the British at Orleans and won the town for the French." Grandmère continued with details of the battle.

"And then what happened?" asked Deborah breathlessly.

"They burned her. They burned her because she said she was responsible only to God and not to the rulers of the Church."

Deborah shuddered, her eyes big with imagining the fate of the brave girl.

"Now tell me about how Harvard College burned."

"That's not news any more. They're rebuilding it now. But I saw with my own eyes how the boys carried books and chairs from the fiery hall last year when I was visiting your uncle in Cambridge. The pox was raging there too. Thank God, we escaped it."

"And now what's happening in Boston?" asked Deborah.

"Riots," said Grandmère darkly. "People are grumbling about the Stamp Act."

"What's that?" asked Deborah.

"You're too young to understand," said Grandmère.

"People are angry with Parliament. But jump down. This is too deep for your head, and I've no more time for you now."

The arrival of Nehemiah was forever etched on Deborah's mind. Years later, probing her memory, she knew it as the first thing she could recall. She even remembered how she had jumped from Grandmère's lap when the old lady had finished telling her of the troubles about the Stamp Act. The baby cried, and Deborah ran to her mother. Mother had stroked her hand tenderly, and then Hannah handed little Nehemiah to Mother to nurse. The baby was funny and helpless-looking as it nuzzled for Mother's breast.

She went outside to her make-believe house which she shared with her stocking doll, her cornhusk Indians, and her soldiers whittled from sticks. Who could be unhappy when the weather was fair and the Indians could scalp the doll and be chased by the soldiers.

A week later she saw the minister in Plympton baptize Nehemiah with water in the name of the Father and the Son and the Holy Ghost.

" 'Tis lucky he is a spring baby. Doubtless he will live," said Cousin Fuller. "Too often the winter babies don't survive the icy christening water."

"Was I a winter baby?" asked Deborah.

"Aye, and a cold day in December it was when they made you a Christian. You were a healthy baby from the start, Deborah."

The day after the christening, Grandmère returned to Uncle Nehemiah's house in Plymouth. Two days later a messenger arrived at daylight with the news that Grandmère was dead of a stroke.

Cousin Fuller, dressed in mourning, took the children, also in black, to the funeral in Plymouth. Deborah clung to Cousin Fuller's hand, too stunned to cry, and heard the minister consign Bathsheba La Broche Bradford to Heaven.

A neighbor had stayed in Plympton with Mother and the baby. When Deborah and Hannah and her brothers came home, Mother was seated by the fire, crying. Deborah began to cry too, putting her eyes on her black skirt as she sat bent over on her little stool.

"Never mind, Mistress Sampson," said the neighbor kindly, "your mother was old and feeble. Sixty-four is a ripe age to reach. Not many of us are that fortunate. And she lived to hold another grandchild on her lap."

"Her life was happy," agreed Mother. "She raised fourteen children and always kept her pride in her French Huguenot father. She often reminded us that she was a highborn French lady. I must not begrudge her her home in Heaven."

Heaven, Heaven, thought Deborah. What must it be like with angels singing everywhere? But she shuddered, recalling the images of Hell that the preachers cried out about and that the Catechism described so vividly.

That night, lying lonely in her trundle bed, Deborah heard Jonny talking in low tones to her mother.

"Do you think Father will be home in time to plant the crops?" he asked in a worried voice.

"How can I tell?" said Mother sadly. "The sea is

a cruel master. He has been gone these seven months, and he thought he would be back long ere the new baby was born."

"I think that Elisha and Eph and I must think of getting the flax and corn planted, and Deborah and Hannah can manage the kitchen garden," said Jonny with authority beyond his years.

"You are a good son, Jonny. This will be hard for the girls."

"Deborah causes twice the trouble of most girls, but she can do twice the work if she has a mind to," said Jonny.

Deborah rose on her elbow and quietly watched Jonny's serious face in the fire glow.

"Mother, is there any chance that we may ever recover the Sampson money that is owed to us?" he asked.

"The Sampson money is gone, and so is the Bradford money," said Mother bitterly. "Your father is a good man and of sweet disposition, son, but he has no head for money. He let his brothers-in-law cheat him out of his inheritance six years ago, before Deborah was born. It was not his fault. Your father was spoiled by a rich father, being an only son with all those sisters and the child of his father's old age to boot. But you're like the Bradfords, every inch, and so is Deborah. If your father does not—but he will come home. Nevertheless, we had better begin to sort our seeds."

And Mother began to cry again while Deborah lay in her small bed with a heart so burdened that she did not

18

go to sleep until the fire had ceased to flicker on the beamed ceiling.

Deborah was digging around the turnip tops that were growing in a neat row in the kitchen garden. She pulled one of the baby radishes and, wiping the dirt from it on her hem, popped the spicy bite into her mouth. Why, the garden was almost hers alone, for Hannah was forever busy helping Mother with the housework and Nehemiah. She turned around to survey her garden. She dropped her hoe and her mouth fell open in a startled gasp. A bearded stranger in sailor togs was striding up the walk.

"Is that my Deborah?" he cried in a deep voice.

Deborah was dumfounded. "Hannah," she squeaked, "it's, it's—"

But before she could finish, her father, smelling of tar and tobacco, swept her into his arms. Hannah came running with three-month-old Nehemiah in her arms. Mother laughed and cried and clung to Father, her face rosy and beautiful.

"Run, run to the field and fetch your brothers, Deborah," said Mother as Father took baby Nehemiah and held him aloft, admiring him.

That night there was such a rejoicing around the Sampson table.

"We were shipwrecked," said Father, helping himself to another piece of the wild turkey that Elisha had shot and smoked. He dressed it with rhubarb sauce, the first of the season, that Mother and Hannah had made the day before. "The ship foundered off New Bedford. Thank God, I was saved, picked up by a whaler that was just setting out. I earned little on that voyage, and I lost all the handsome profits I had made on the first trip. But we have something to be thankful for."

He threw a whaleskin wallet of money on the table and continued.

"I have a new berth on a whaler leaving New Bedford in late August. Not many ships are leaving Boston now with times so hard there. Oh, this trip will make me rich again, Deborah," he said to Mother. "And you, little Deborah, will have red shoes to match your red cheeks, and you, Hannah, shall have a silken gown, and all the boys will have guns for their hunting."

"But must you go again, Jonathan?" pleaded Mother. "Life is so hard without you."

"This will be my last voyage," promised Father. "This time I will return with enough money to pay our debts and more besides, and the troubles will be ended in the Sampson household."

"Pray God it may be so," murmured Mother, turning away to hide her fear-crossed face.

Father stayed until late August, working in the fields with the boys from early morning to dusk. Deborah and Hannah weeded the garden and helped in the flax fields. Life was happy with Father at home.

"Mother, you look pretty again, and Jonny is like

his old self. I never need to 'look out the window' now," commented Deborah as she sat at the table spooning corn-meal mush into her ever-hungry mouth. "And Hannah is fun again."

It must be fun to be nine and have a new calico dress like the one Father got for Hannah on her birthday.

Father was always full of news. He and Jonny hurried in from the village two days before Father was to leave.

"More trouble in Boston," he said, dipping his hands into the wooden tub beside the well and sloshing water over his hot face. "Lieutenant Governor Hutchinson's house was looted and ruined."

"Why? Who did it?" asked Deborah excitedly.

"Mobs," said Father. "Mobs protesting the Stamp Act. They say Governor Hutchinson's little daughters barely escaped with their lives."

"Why? Why? Why?" demanded Deborah. "What's a Stamp Act?" Grandmère had talked of it, she remembered.

"Oh, drat the child," said Father in exasperation. "Well, it's something Parliament wants to impose on the Colonies to raise money, and the Colonies don't think it's fair. Now don't ask me any more questions." Father gave her an affectionate pat.

After Father left, Mother's woebegone face and Nehemiah's fretful cries chased even the lingering happy memories from the house.

"Mother's milk has given out," Hannah confided to Deborah as they sat cooling under the apple tree in September after gathering the apples for drying. "She has hired a wet nurse to come and feed Nehemiah. Do you know what that means, Deborah?"

Deborah shook her head. Hannah, looking wise beyond her nine years, whispered in Deborah's ear. "I think Mother is with child again. I heard her tell Cousin Fuller that she thought there would be another baby here come next April."

"Oh, no!" cried Deborah. "Nehemiah is baby enough here. I like Nehemiah well enough now, but I don't think I should fancy another one."

"Hush, Deborah, that's wicked talk. God sends babies, and we must love them."

"Why?" asked Deborah.

"Because it's God's will." Hannah's tired voice was on the breaking point. "And because life is hard," she added with premature sadness.

In October Jonny reported that representatives of nine of the Colonies had met in New York to protest the Stamp Act Father had talked about last summer.

"Where's New York?" asked Deborah. "Is it beyond Boston? Beyond London?"

"Far beyond," Jonny, who had scant knowledge himself of where New York lay, said importantly. It was far away, many days by stage or post rider. That he knew, for he had seen the weary passengers stop at the tavern.

"They say that there are Sons of Liberty groups arising everywhere," added Jonny. "Even in Plympton. They ask people not to buy British goods."

"As if we could buy any goods at all," said Elisha sourly.

"Why?" asked Deborah as usual.

"Why what?" said Jonny irritably. "I can't answer all your questions, Deborah."

Deborah pulled the cat's tail and tripped Eph, and then wished she hadn't when Mother ordered her sharply to go sit in the cold corner. Thus went fall into winter.

On the seventeenth of December, snow was piled against the door. Seventeen sixty-five was almost over. Cold air seeped through the floor boards and around the window edges. Deborah sat by the fire with Nehemiah in her lap, dipping clean rags into a dish of warm milk for the baby to suck. He was eight months old now, healthy and happy, and no longer in need of the wet nurse.

Deborah bounced him on her knee. She liked him now, liked seeing his wide toothy grin when Hannah spooned gruel into his mouth. Deborah herself had made him a teething necklace from fawns' teeth. Only occasionally did she recall the hazy notion of being laid on the shelf because a baby boy had taken her place.

Hannah took the baby from Deborah, who sat idly on her stool, trying not to think of Grandmère in her cold grave under the snow. She tried to think of something new and exciting to do before Mother found her idle and set her to learning the Catechism.

"Elisha," Mother would say, "fetch the SPIRITUAL MILK and catechize Deborah." Deborah hated the ugly little book. She could see it now, there on the shelf, MILK

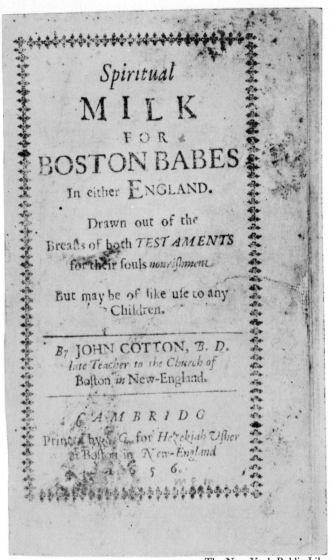

Facsimile of cover of *Spiritual Milk* . . .

Queſt. *How doth the Miniſtry of the Goſpell help you in this curſed E-ſtate?*

x Luke 3. 4,5,6.

Anſw. By humbling me (x) yet more, and then rayſing me up out of this Eſtate.

Queſt. *How doth the Miniſtry of the Goſpel humble you more?*

w 2 Tim: 1.10. 1 Tim:1. 15. John 16.7, 9. & 6.44. Luk.19.10

Anſw. By revealing the [w] Grace of the Lord Jeſus, in dying to ſave ſinners: and yet convincing me of my ſinn, in not believing on him, and of my utter inſufficiency, to come to him; And ſo I feel my ſelf utterly loſt.

Queſt. *How then doth the Miniſtry of the Goſpell rayſe you up out of this loſt eſtate to come unto Chriſt?*

z John 12. 32. 2 Cor:5. 19,20. Cant:5.10. to 16. with 1.1. 2 Cor:3.28 Luk.19.10 Mat:9.13 Gal.3.5. Rom:10. 14. ʋ 1.16

Anſw. By (a) teaching me the value and the vertue of the death of Chriſt, and the riches of his Grace to loſt ſinners: By revealing the promiſe of Grace to ſuch, (and by miniſtring the Spirit of Grace, to apply Chriſt, and his promiſe of grace unto my ſelf, and to keep me in him.

Q: *How doth the Spirit of grace ap-*

B

Facsimile of one page of text.

FOR BABES DRAWN OUT OF THE BREASTS OF BOTH TESTA-
MENTS, CHIEFLY FOR THE SPIRITUAL NOURISHMENT OF
BOSTON BABES IN EITHER ENGLAND, BUT MAY BE OF LIKE
USE FOR ANY CHILDREN, by John Cotton. Everybody had
to learn it.

Eph stopped beside her, warming his hands by the
fire. Deborah sighed, her eye falling on the dusky shelf
in the corner. Without knowing why herself, Deborah
jumped from the stool and pushed Eph to the floor. They
lay wrestling on the rag carpet, pulling hair, kicking,
punching, and squealing, half with laughter and half
with excitement.

"Children, children!" cried Mother, who leaned
over them, tired-eyed and big-waisted with her unborn
child. "Stop it. Stop it this instant."

There was a knock on the door. Eph and Deborah
broke off their fight and raced to the door while Mother,
close to tears, smoothed her apron and straightened the
rug. Who could it be? Visitors were rare in this kind of
weather.

"Why, 'tis Cousin Fuller!" cried Deborah, opening the door. Cousin Fuller, red-cheeked and puffing
frosted air, shook the snow from her cloak and removed
her cowhide overboots and drew up to the fire with the
family.

Deborah stood beside her, delighted at the diver-
sion, while Mother set out the teapot.

"What brings you out on such a day, Cousin?"
asked Mother. " 'Tis a treat to have a visitor on such a
snowy day."

"I was put in mind of a day," said Cousin Fuller, stretching her hands to the fire. "The day was five years ago, and Miss Deborah Sampson was born in the world. I recall she had a good horoscope, being born under the sign of Sagittarius. Those born under that sign have a zest for travel and adventure. I remember she was such a sturdy baby."

"Happen that was so. I quite forgot. Deborah, child, this is your birthday," said Mother.

Deborah looked around with a new sense of importance. "You mean I am five years old now? Why, I'm almost as old as Eph now."

"Devil take her. I'll get even with you yet," mumbled Eph.

"Ephraim," said Mother sternly. "I shall not bear with such talk."

"Children been having a bit of a scuffle, eh?" said Cousin Fuller glancing at the disheveled children and the overturned stool.

Mother sank down on the settle beside Cousin Fuller. "Sometimes 'tis more than I can bear," she said with a catch in her voice. "It's hard on the children without a father. Hannah growing old before her time, Elisha and Jonny doing men's work, Eph and Deborah bickering the day through, and not enough time to teach them or enough money to send them to school. Deborah should be in dame school."

"Aye, she has an able mind, that one," said Cousin Fuller. "Cousin, I have come to make a suggestion to you. I know that charity sets ill with a Bradford or a

Sampson, but as I am maiden and childless, give me Deborah to live with me. I can school her in books and domestic matters, as I have plenty of time to nurture her mind. Besides, it would be a help to me to have someone to fetch and carry and keep me company. For all you love the child, it would help you to let her come to me for a while."

Deborah held her breath, looking from Mother to Cousin Fuller, astonished by the idea. To live with Cousin Fuller, to sleep in the feather bed and have sugar cookies and lessons, what a wonderful thought. But to leave home, to be sent away, to desert the crowded fireside, to leave Hannah and Mother and the brothers? Mother wouldn't permit it. Of course not.

But Mother sat silent, gazing past the people in the room and out the frosted window to where the road met the horizon.

"I thank you, Cousin. Of course I couldn't *give* you Deborah. Not unless"—there was a catch in her voice—"not unless it comes to putting the children out on the town." She tried to say it lightly.

Put out on the town? Deborah stared at her mother. What an idea. Only paupers were put out on the town for charitable people to take in to save them from starvation and freezing.

"Put out on the town?" echoed Hannah, her face turning white.

"Oh, of course not," said Mother hastily. "Your father will be home before many months with a big bag of money. What am I thinking of? I'm only looking on the gloomy side. But Cousin, if Deborah desires it, I would thank you if she could visit you until Jonathan's ship comes in. We have many mouths to feed now, and with one more, come spring, my strength and patience are sorely tried. 'Tis more than I manage some days to keep from becoming a common scold."

"Would you like to come with me, my girl?" asked Cousin Fuller, stirring her tea with a pewter spoon and trying not to look at Deborah's uncertain, troubled face.

"If Mother wants it," said Deborah slowly. She loved Cousin Fuller, kind and generous as she was, but little cold prickles of hurt pinched her heart as she tied her extra garments, her drawers, her white knitted stockings, her Sunday apron, and her summer dress into a bundle.

Mother put her arm around Deborah. "You shall come home and visit often. When the weather is better, you can come every day."

Deborah nodded, not daring to speak. It had all happened so fast, to be a visitor at home, not to live there any more. Dry-eyed, she let out her breath in a long sigh.

"Good-by, Mother," she said. "I will come and see you soon."

II

*1766–1768: In 1766 the Colonists forced the
repeal of the Stamp Act.*

I am five years old, thought Deborah with a sense of ela-
tion as she sat at the table that night with Cousin Fuller
and her cousin's silent brother, Mr. Fuller.

"I would buy you a present for your birthday if
times were not so hard," said Cousin Fuller. "I don't see
how your poor mother has managed to feed you."

Deborah ate greedily. Mother had not managed to
feed them very well lately. Deborah dropped a few dried

apples in her pocket to take to Hannah and Eph when she went home to visit. Cousin Fuller saw her do it, but she laughed and agreed to it. Deborah was careful not to let her see her wet eyes when she went to bed.

The days passed quickly. Deborah studied her Primer sitting on the stool at Cousin Fuller's feet. She began to learn the Catechism of the Assembly of Divines in the back of the Primer. Sometimes Cousin Fuller would tell her stories from the Bible in an entertaining fashion that made them very different from the dry readings she heard at endless Sunday meetings.

She began to learn to spin and sew and make a loaf of bread. The weather was so cold and the snows were so deep that her visits home were rare events. For weeks she stayed indoors at Cousin Fuller's, only stepping outside to help Mr. Fuller with the milking and to gather the goose eggs. The old goose and gander pecked at her when she stepped into the barn, but she learned to shake her apron at them and send them flying into the sheep pen.

"That Deborah, she's fearless," said Mr. Fuller, watching her trudge through the snow on her way to visit her mother one day in February. "I don't see how her mother could have spared her."

"Her mother has more children than places to put them or food to fill them. I don't see how I ever got along without Deborah, the help she is with her fetching and carrying. What I intended as an act of godly charity has been a blessing since the day she came here. When, if, her father comes home, I dread the hour that they take her from me."

Mr. Fuller stared silently into the fire. For a man to go to sea for a living was a gamble at best. Perhaps Deborah would be here longer than his sister thought. Her huffing and puffing was caused by too much rich blood, the Boston surgeon had said, but she stubbornly refused to be leeched. It was good she had the child here to help her.

On the first day of April, Deborah sat in the kitchen doorway eating her breakfast while tender sunshine flooded about her. Eph came running into the yard, quite breathless.

"Hannah and Nehemiah are coming," he panted. "Jonny has gone to fetch the granny woman, and Aunt Hannah is at our house to help born the new baby."

"Cousin Fuller, here they come," shouted Deborah, running out to meet Hannah, who was struggling up the road with the wriggling Nehemiah in her arms. Hannah set him down, and he went to Deborah on his wobbly legs. Together the sisters walked to the house with the baby between them, holding his hands.

By nightfall Elisha came to tell them they had a new sister who was to be called Sylvia.

On the nineteenth of May, 1766, Deborah was awakened by the sound of the church bell ringing wildly.

"What's happening?" she cried, leaping from her bed and running out the door in her bare feet and undershift.

"For shame, miss. Get back in the house and cover

yourself," scolded Cousin Fuller, who was by the well. "You're as bad as a hobbledehoy running about in your drawers."

"Why are the bells ringing?" persisted Deborah.

"Brother has gone to find out. He left off the milking and ran to town. I must finish it myself, it seems, unless—"

But Deborah had darted into the house to hurry into her dress. She splashed water on her face and ran to find Mr. Fuller.

"Parliament has repealed the Stamp Act!" he cried, his voice loud with excitement. "The rider came into town to tell that Boston has gone wild with joy and that bells are ringing in all the churches, that the ships are firing salutes, and the town is being hung with flags. People have been dancing in the streets since midnight, and the Boston Liberty Tree is strung with flags."

"Oh, how I wish I could see it all. How I would like to go to Boston! Cousin, could I visit my mother this day? She might not know the news," pleaded Deborah.

"Oh, she'll know the news, I'll wager, but go ahead. I know you are wanting to see the baby again. 'Tis over a week since you were there. But first eat your breakfast, and I'll pour up a pitcher of cider for your mother. We have more than enough left from the fall."

Deborah watched Cousin Fuller fill the tall pitcher with cool cider from the barrel in the root cellar. She smiled a little when she realized that this was the very pitcher that had sat on the shelf and terrified her the day Nehemiah was born. It seemed a long time ago.

Deborah found Mother and Hannah talking about the news as they worked in the garden. Nehemiah was playing in the dirt under the apple tree, and Sylvia was asleep in the cradle by the kitchen door.

"Where does Nehemiah sleep?" asked Deborah, looking down at the rosy baby in the cradle.

"Nehemiah sleeps in the trundle bed now," said Hannah.

"Maybe I won't ever sleep in it again," said Deborah wistfully. Much as she loved Cousin Fuller, she hoped in her heart that living with her was only temporary because Father would return to reunite the family and restore their fortune.

"May happen not. Let's go fetch Jonny and Elisha from the field so they can share the cider," said Hannah quickly.

"Where's Eph?" asked Deborah as they set out, half running.

"Deborah, Eph has gone to live with Aunt Hannah. I didn't want to say it in front of Mother, for she is very downhearted about it, but Uncle Nehemiah has been to see her. They talked late into the night. They fear that Father is not coming back."

"Why?" asked Deborah, her face turning white and her heart stopping in mid-beat. "Father said—"

"I know, but Uncle Nehemiah says the ship that Father was on is reported to have been wrecked. The wreckage landed on Nantucket, they say, and they found no survivors." Hannah's voice broke, and she turned her face away.

"You mean," said Deborah, swallowing the gorge that rose in her throat, "that Father isn't coming back and that our family is going to be put on the town?"

"Hush, don't say that to Mother," warned Hannah. "Mother has written to Uncle Elisha to see if Jonny and Elisha can go live there, and Uncle Nehemiah has offered to take Mother and the babies and me to live in Plymouth. His wife is ailing and Mother will run his house. You will stay with Cousin Fuller forever, I guess."

"And our house?" asked Deborah, looking back at it over her shoulder, fearfully.

"Our house doesn't belong to us any more," said Hannah. "Father borrowed some money, and now the man is going to take the house instead because we can't pay him back."

Deborah stepped behind a chokecherry thicket and vomited. She never forgot the repeal of the Stamp Act because she never felt like a child again after that day.

Sometimes in the two years that followed Deborah got messages from her mother, who was living in Plymouth. On the town they were, but at least they were farmed out with relatives. How shameful it would be to have one's name read out in the town meeting and the people asked to take the objects of charity into their homes as public charges.

Deborah had seen the cart go by with their belongings piled on it headed for Uncle Nehemiah's house. She had stood dry-eyed in Cousin Fuller's yard waving good-by to Mother and Hannah and the babies, all of whom were crying. Eph, Elisha, and Jonny had already gone. Another family moved into their old house. Father would never return, of that she was now certain.

She was seven years old. There was little need for crying over the past because Cousin Fuller continued to love her and instruct her, the food was plentiful, and the clothing was warm.

Cousin Fuller never tired of teaching her to spin and weave. Deborah learned to recognize the best wool, to knit the finest stockings, and to hatchel the best flax for making linen. But Cousin Fuller was often tired. Her breathing became a labored effort, and her rosy complexion turned an apoplectic red when she busied herself too strenuously with the work about the place. Gradually Deborah became almost the housekeeper, washing the dishes, churning the butter, feeding the poultry, and weeding the garden.

"What would I do without you?" said Cousin Fuller gratefully, pulling from her pocket a sweetmeat that she had bought from the peddler man who stopped by their house on his route from the Boston docks.

Deborah grinned, thanking her cousin for the gift. She knew what she would do with it. Isaiah Cushman had a baby piglet, and Isaiah was such a pig himself that he might be persuaded to trade the candy for the piglet. Then she would bring it home and raise it. Mr. Fuller would not object; indeed, it would amuse him. Then she could sell the pig in the autumn and put the money away or maybe send it to Mother. It was a good thing to have money hidden away, but it might be a better thing to give it away, she reflected, struggling with her conscience.

When she got the money she decided to give it to Mother after all. In mid-December she went for a visit to Plymouth. Cousin Fuller thought of it. There was little snow yet this winter, and as Aunt Laurana McFarland was driving her cart to Plymouth, Cousin Fuller asked that Deborah be allowed to go along and spend her eighth birthday with Mother.

Joyously they packed a bag of gifts for Mother and Hannah and the babies. There was a sacque that Deborah had knitted from her own spun wool for Sylvia, and there were the new breeches that Cousin Fuller had made from an old scrap for Nehemiah.

"He's full young for breeches," Cousin Fuller had objected when Deborah suggested it.

"But if you wait until he's older, then he'll be too big for breeches made from this piece," said Deborah practically.

Cousin Fuller agreed. She also donated a flowered kerchief for Hannah, who at twelve already looked like a proper young woman. Deborah filled her needlework bag with the gifts, and then with a rush of emotion, half of regret and half of joy at her own generosity, she tied the pig money in a handkerchief for Mother. What need had she for money here in the prosperous household of Cousin Fuller.

Mother held Deborah close and thanked her for the gifts.

"I didn't forget your birthday this time," she said. "Hannah and I have knitted you a pair of stockings in a lace pattern."

Early in the morning as she lay warm and safe in the bed between Mother and Hannah, Sylvia and Nehemiah being crowded in the old trundle bed, her uncle came into the room and called Mother into the kitchen. They talked together out of word-hearing but in tones strong enough to bring Deborah onto her elbow to listen alertly to the sound of alarm that came through to her.

Mother came heavily back into the room and looked steadily at Deborah.

"Courage, child. Get your things on. A messenger has just come from Plympton, and we are going back with him. Cousin Fuller, God rest her blessed soul, has died of an apoplectic stroke. Hannah can take care of the young ones. We must go and see that the funeral is decently done."

Deborah shivered as she sat through the long funeral oration in the Congregational Church. Even with Mother beside her weeping into her handkerchief Deborah felt a sense of utter disbelief.

Only three days ago Cousin Fuller had slipped a packet of cookies into Deborah's pocket as she had set out on her trip. Ruddy-faced, bustling Cousin Fuller— could her kindness and jolly spirits be gone forever?

The knot inside her would not erupt into tears, but

38

it spread into a general misery that paralyzed her limbs so that Mother had to pull her to her feet when the black-clad minister exhorted them to stand in prayer. Deborah remembered the day long ago when she had risen to watch Grandmère's body borne out to the burying ground. Cousin Fuller had stood by her then.

Perhaps she might find comfort in looking through the high window. She drew herself up tall, but she could only see a patch of cheerless gray winter sky. Deborah clung to her mother's hand, and finally tears began to flood her cheeks.

The next day she and Mother cleaned Cousin Fuller's house, put her things in order, packed Deborah's clothes in a linen sack, and bid Mr. Fuller good-by.

"What's to become of the child?" asked Mr. Fuller. "I'm sorry that it won't do for me, a bachelor, to keep her here."

"I don't know," said Mother. "I must find her another place."

"I'll miss the lass," said Mr. Fuller. "Deborah is a good hand at anything that comes along, as helpful as one twice her age."

"What will you do, Mr. Fuller? Who will tend your house and do your washing and mending?" asked Deborah anxiously.

"Happen I have a nephew newly-married needing a place to live. I talked with him and his wife at the funeral feast. They will live here and look after the house and help on the farm. I need a young man for the heavy work, with my hands getting so stiff."

Deborah went back to Plymouth with Mother. Night after night she squeezed into the narrow bed between Mother and Hannah, while by day Mother looked for a place for Deborah. She couldn't stay forever at Uncle Nehemiah's for his charity was already stretched to the limit.

Who wanted a fatherless girl? Even looking out the window at the glittering snow and the brown winter birds failed to help. Mother tried to cheer her.

"It's Christmas Day," she said one morning. "When I was a child I visited Boston. I had a friend who was an Episcopalian who took me to King's Chapel on Christmas. The church was all bedecked with greens and candles. My aunt was very cross with me when she found I had been there, saying that the celebration of Christmas went against the Puritan religion. But I always remembered it, and I have learned since that they celebrate Christmas in old England and in some of the Colonies with glee and 'decking the halls with holly,' as the saying goes. I sometimes wonder if it is so sinful to put a little joy in the church."

The thought of anything as outrageous as a decorated church brought a smile to Deborah's face. She put her handkerchief in her pocket and continued helping with the housework. There was no time for grief when she had to earn her keep in Uncle Nehemiah's household.

One morning in January, Mistress Sampson had a

caller, the minister from the Congregational Church in Plymouth.

"Mistress Sampson," he said. "I have learned of the situation of your daughter. Summon the child, as I may have a solution."

Mother called Deborah from the bedchamber where she was playing with Sylvia and Nehemiah, crawling on the floor with the little ones taking turns riding on her back.

Deborah smoothed her black dress and adjusted her black kerchief on her fair hair and followed her mother into the kitchen where the minister sat on the settle by the fire. He stared sternly at her as she dropped him a curtsy.

"Do you read, girl?" he asked.

Deborah nodded, mystified.

"What is the chief end of man?" he asked.

"Man's chief end is to glorify God and enjoy him forever," replied Deborah automatically.

"What rule hath God given to direct us how we may glorify God and enjoy him?" asked the minister, keeping his hawklike eyes upon her.

"The word of gold which is contained in the scriptures old and new Testament is the only rule to direct us how we may glorify and enjoy him," said Deborah, looking straight back at him.

"Ah," said the minister, rubbing his hands together, " 'tis plain you have studied your Catechism, and you are a strong one and large in body, albeit a bit young. However, I hear good tales of your accomplishments.

Mistress Sampson, an opportunity has arisen whereby the child may earn her keep in a good home over in Middleborough."

"I thank you for your interest, sir," said Mistress Sampson. "Middleborough is many miles from here, fifteen or more."

"But when a child is dependent on charity, she must go where the door is opened," said the minister piously.

"Alas, it is to charity that we must look these days," agreed Mother sadly.

"I can earn my way, sir," spoke up Deborah. Dependent on charity indeed!

Mother put a restraining hand on Deborah's arm. "Excuse her, sir. She's only a child and does not understand how difficult it is to find a charitable home."

"Listen to your elders, miss," said the minister. " 'The eye that mocketh his father and despiseth the instruction of his mother let the ravens of the valley pluck it out and the young eagles eat it.' "

Deborah shuddered and dropped her eyes. Charity, she thought angrily. I shall learn how to earn money and I won't depend on anyone else. I'll earn my way even if I am a girl.

"Kindly tell me what person in Middleborough is interested in Deborah?" said Mother.

"Madam Thacher, relict of the Reverend Peter Thacher. She needs a young person to cheer and aid her in her solitary old age, especially one who can read. The Reverend Mr. Conant of the Middleborough Church wrote me about her."

"Madam Thacher? But is she not very old and bed-ridden besides?" said Mother doubtfully.

"Very old and feeble," agreed the minister, "but she expressed an interest in the child. Some relation of the late Mistress Fuller told Madam Thacher that this child was capable and could work in exchange for her keep."

Mother looked like one of the trapped birds that mean boys shut up in tight cages. Deborah at that moment felt suddenly older than her mother. This obviously would not be a happy place like Cousin Fuller's, but at least it was a place. Mother could not afford to be soft-hearted and refuse it.

"Please, sir, let me speak for my mother," said Deborah clearly. "I should like to go to Madam Thacher's. There is no room for me here. I thank Madam Thacher for her interest in me."

"Well spoken, lass," said the minister. "I shall fetch you tomorrow."

"Mother, do you remember the little verse that Grandmère used to say about looking out the window?" asked Deborah as they watched the minister going down the road.

"Of course," said Mother. "It comes to me often."

"I say it too," said Deborah. "I think it helps more than saying prayers."

"That's wicked talk," said Mother. "But it does no harm to do both. Keep watching out the window, Deborah. I wish a great future for you, but you will have to make your own way."

The old minister halted his horse at Uncle Nehemiah's house early the next morning. Deborah swung herself up behind him, her few belongings tied in a kerchief. She wrapped her cloak tightly around herself and grasped the forbidding black back. She kept her face straight ahead, as she could not bear to see Mother's tears.

"We are grateful, sir," said Mother.

" 'Tis plainly my duty," replied the minister.

He gave the horse a kick and headed into the icy wind.

III

1769–1770: The Boston Massacre occurred in 1770.

Deborah was stiff with cold when they dismounted in front of Madam Thacher's house in Middleborough. They were ushered into the dark kitchen where Madam Thacher sat wrapped in a blanket by the fire, a toothless wrinkled old woman who peered at Deborah through dim eyes. Madam Thacher's niece, a sullen, plump, young woman, blew up the fire and set the best chair for the minister. She looked disapprovingly at Deborah.

"I fear you are over young for what must be done here," she said with no change of expression. She showed Deborah where to put her bundle. Deborah shivered.

"Do you live here?" she asked the woman. "What are you called?"

"Put only one question to me at a time, miss. Yes, I live here because I must. I am called Zillah."

Zillah took the tea canister from the shelf and laid out the cups and pot. Water was boiling in the iron kettle over the fire.

"Oh, tea will taste good," said Deborah, rubbing her blue fingers together and breathing on them.

"I shall serve you this time," said Zillah ungraciously, "but don't expect me to be waiting on you. You're here to work, and don't forget it."

Deborah looked stonily at Zillah and then moved to the window, where she put her eye to the peephole in the shutter. There was nobody in sight on the wind-swept snow, but a red-gold sun brightened the winter horizon. Deborah felt her heart lift a little.

"Move to the fire, if you will," ordered Zillah.

Deborah turned back to the gloomy room. Zillah pushed a mug of steaming tea at her, and Deborah sat down on the footstool to drink it.

"Fetch some bread for the minister and some for the child too, Zillah," said Madam Thacher in her high voice. "Move closer to me, child, so I may touch you."

Deborah moved closer to the paper-white, blue-veined, bony old hand of Madam Thacher, who trem-

46

blingly tried to stroke Deborah's wind-blown braid. Deborah stiffened and tried to suppress a shudder.

"I hope she will prove adequate," said the minister, relaxing a little with the hot tea down his throat. "To place her here will serve two ends: to find a Christian home for this fatherless child and to meet the needs of the relict of a man of God."

Old Madam Thacher nodded her head and continued to nod until her eyes closed and she drooped her head against the cushions. Her breath came in the little snorting gasps of the quick naps of the very old.

The minister sipped his tea, and Zillah quietly refilled his cup. Deborah sat without moving, feeling her frozen blood begin to thaw and pound through her body. She was suddenly very tired, and her mouth flew open in an involuntary yawn just as Madam Thacher awoke.

The minister stood up. "I must go to Mr. Conant's house. He expects me on the Lord's business. Attend to your duties, Deborah, and you will be richly rewarded in Heaven."

I'd rather be rewarded right now, thought Deborah. Her stomach yearned for more tea and bread, and a bite of meat and potato would taste good beyond measure.

The door that closed behind the minister let in a cold blast of winter air that flickered the fire and blew ashes on the rug.

"Brush up the ashes, child," said Madam Thacher in her quavery voice.

Deborah reached for the sedge broom and whisked

the ashes back into the fireplace. Her mouth watered as she smelled the stew simmering in the black pot over the fire.

"Might I serve you a dish of stew, Madam Thacher?" she asked hopefully.

"Bless me, yes," said the old lady. "Prepare one for yourself, too."

Zillah was moving about in the next room.

"Mistress Zillah, Madam Thacher wants me to serve her some supper. Shall I serve you as well?"

"The old lady is daft. It should not be her supper time for two hours more. But feed her if she likes. I have an errand to do in the village. Goodness knows, I've spent enough dreary hours with her."

"It must be hard to be old and always wrapped in blankets," said Deborah thoughtfully.

"Enough of your pert talk," said Zillah. "She's yours for the next two hours. Tomorrow you can be useful again with the monthly washing."

Zillah scurried out the back door, and within three minutes Deborah had served two dishes. She ate her own portion so fast that she did not notice that Madam Thacher's fingers were unsteady on the spoon. Deborah gently wiped off the spilled spots of gravy and fed her the rest while the old lady smacked with her toothless gums.

"Do you know I am old, child?" asked Madam Thacher.

"Oh, yes, Madam, I guessed it," said Deborah, smiling to herself.

"I was not always old. Before my eyes went dim and my mind became chancy, I read many things. They tell me you can read, a very good thing for a miss to do. Zillah reads poorly. Fetch a book, fetch THE PILGRIM'S PROGRESS. I admire Mr. Bunyan."

Deborah pulled the stool to the high shelf so she could reach the books. There was a big Bible, THE ESSAYS OF JOHN LOCKE, many books of sermons, and other worn volumes whose titles Deborah could not see. She found the right book, and laid it open on her lap.

" 'As I walked through the wilderness of this world,' " she began as she read the adventures of Christian and Evangelist.

Presently when Madam Thacher's snoring told her that she was asleep, Deborah continued to read to herself by the firelight. When Zillah returned much later Deborah helped move Madam Thacher to her bed. She fell into her own bed nine-tenths asleep before Zillah blew out the candle.

Days at Madam Thacher's were an endless blurring chain of work and increasing responsibility as Zillah took more and more advantage of Deborah. Black clad and uncombed, Deborah emptied the slops and tended the fire. She swept the floor and did more than her share of the monthly washing. Before spring she had grown tall and thin, her face pale as a winter root.

She gritted her teeth against the bitter retorts that rose to her tongue when Zillah berated her for burning too many candles or eating too many of the apples stored in the root cellar. She stood with her back to the room many times a day, looking out the window.

As Zillah could scarcely decipher words, and in any case she could read no sense into them, the reading fell to Deborah. The bookshelf became her private passion while Zillah seethed. There was no chance to visit Mother, and letters came seldom, for paper was too dear.

One morning in September as Zillah slammed the dasher up and down in the churn, Deborah prepared to read to Madam Thacher. She swallowed a sigh as she picked up the Bible, glancing beyond Zillah at the inviting open door. How wonderful it would be to run barefoot in the grass and loosen her tight braids and let her hair blow about.

"Read me from the beginning," said the old lady in a querulous voice.

"But Madam Thacher, I have read the first chapter of Genesis every day for the past fortnight. Could we not proceed to the next chapter?" pleaded Deborah. How terribly the old lady's mind was failing.

"No, I want to start at the beginning," she said childishly.

Zillah blurted out a short, mirthless, grunt of laughter, but she stopped when a shadow filled the doorway.

"Good morning," called the Reverend Mr. Conant cheerily as he stepped into the room. "What, reading the

Holy Writ?" he said approvingly.

"Yes, sir," said Deborah, rising and closing the Bible. "Madam Thacher likes the first chapter of Genesis, and we have read it until I know it with the pages closed."

Mr. Conant looked at the wan little girl, the dull-faced Zillah, and the senile Madam Thacher. A poor place for a child, but what else could be done? A penniless, fatherless, child must work or starve, but what a quick mind she had.

"So you know the beginning of Genesis with the covers closed. How then is your memory of the Catechism?"

"I have not studied it since I came here to live, sir, and that has been nearly a year ago," said Deborah.

"Why have you not seen to her learning?" he said impatiently to Zillah. "Madam Thacher is not capable of seeing to it." Madam Thacher had dropped off into one of her naps.

"I can teach her nothing, sir," said Zillah resentfully. "She knows it all and is at no pains to hide it."

Mr. Conant sighed. It was God's world, but too little love lay in it.

"Deborah, you must learn the Catechism as set out by the Assembly of Divines. When you have learned it all so that you can repeat the answers without mistakes, then I shall give you a book of your own."

He looked at the cheerless child, and a frivolous thought ran through his Puritan mind. "My young friend

Henry Knox has lately opened a bookstore in Boston. Perhaps I might order you a book about the fantastic travels of Lemuel Gulliver."

"Oh, dear Mr. Conant!" cried Deborah with such joy that she ran across the room and grasped his hand. "I would like that better than anything in the world."

That evening before dark Madam Thacher was asleep in her bed, Zillah was out visiting as usual, and Deborah sat by the window with THE SHORTER CATE-CHISM OF THE ASSEMBLY OF DIVINES in her lap. There were but one hundred and seven questions to answer, and Cousin Fuller had taught her the first six.

Girls who went to school could learn the Catechism there, but school was not for her, a child who was a public charge. She leafed through the book and read Question Nineteen.

Q. Did God leave all mankind to perish in the state of Sin and Misery?
A. God having out of his meet good pleasure from all eternity elected some to everlasting life did enter into a Covenant of Grace to deliver them out of the state of Sin and Misery and to bring them into a state of Salvation by a Redeemer.

Deborah tried not to think what the thing meant. Oh well, she had only to learn it, not to understand it.

She studied early and late, so that in December on her ninth birthday she knocked on Mr. Conant's door and stood timidly in the kitchen. It had been so long since

Deborah had been out of the Thacher house, for she was even required to stay at home on Sundays with Madam Thacher while Zillah went to meeting, that she tingled with excitement at seeing a new face and another fireplace.

"Please, ma'am, I have come to say my Catechism to Mr. Conant," she told the servant woman.

"First sit and warm yourself and eat a bite of gingerbread," said the woman kindly. Deborah made it last as long as possible, savoring it to the last crumb.

Mr. Conant called her into his study, settled down in his chair, and began to question her. It was an hour later when he asked her Question One Hundred and Seven.

"Splendid," he exclaimed. "You have answered it all perfectly."

Deborah gave her first smile in months when he put the book in her hand.

"TRAVELS INTO SEVERAL REMOTE NATIONS OF THE WORLD, BY LEMUEL GULLIVER," she read.

"Jonathan Swift wrote it, although it does not say so," said Mr. Conant.

"Thank you, Mr. Conant. This is the nicest present I've ever had, and today, by chance, is my birthday."

When she returned home in triumph with the book, Zillah feigned great disinterest, but Deborah laughed to herself when later she found Zillah secretly examining the tiny illustrations.

One morning in March, Mr. Conant stopped by

the Thacher house. "How would you like to go visit your mother tomorrow, Deborah?" he asked.

"Oh, sir, nothing would suit me better!" cried Deborah.

"Your mother sent asking for you to come to Plymouth this week, as your brothers will be there. It would be a rare reunion for you. Happen Deacon Thomas is going that way tomorrow, and he can take you in his cart. It has been over a year since you saw your family."

Deborah packed a small bundle of clothing along with her precious book. How they would all listen to the story of Gulliver and the Lilliputians and the giant horses.

"You are too thin, child," Mother said, looking at her at arm's length after Deacon Thomas had left her off at the door. "Your color is pale and your eyes are too hollow for my old Deborah." Mother looked worried.

Deborah saw her mother's careworn face and decided not to spill out her pent-up annoyances with Zillah. What could Mother do about it except take more worries onto her already overburdened shoulders.

But that night they were merry as they sat listening for the footsteps that might be Jonny and Elisha. Nehemiah and Sylvia crawled over Deborah, begging for more stories and one more look at the book.

"If only I could see Eph," said Deborah.

"Eph is eleven now," said Mother. "I hear he is big and strong for his age. I'm sad that he could not come this time."

It was mid-morning on the sixth of March when a great clatter at the kitchen door told them that Jonny and Elisha had arrived. Jonny, now a Boston printer's apprentice and big and handsome at eighteen, grabbed Deborah and swung her off her feet despite her long legs and her nine-year-old dignity. Elisha, who was soon to leave for his first sea voyage, as taciturn as ever, stood behind swinging his cap on his finger and grinning. Mother cried a little and looked at her strapping sons, who were now almost grown men.

"Is it true, Elisha, that you are going to sea, across the ocean to see the world?" asked Deborah enviously, thinking of her irksome life with Madam Thacher and Zillah.

Elisha swaggered about the kitchen a bit, lording it over Jonny, who would be left behind in Boston. "Sure, that's why I'm home, so you can all tell me good-by before I go to exciting places."

"You don't need to get on a ship for excitement," said Jonny, stretching his long legs to the fire as he dropped down on the settle beside Uncle Nehemiah, now old and a widower. "Wait 'til I tell you what happened in Boston last night. It's lucky we got here at all."

"Why? What happened?" asked Deborah eagerly. She felt alive again with the babel of voices and lively people buzzing about her.

"Old Deb hasn't changed," laughed Jonny. "It's still why, why, why."

"Murder," said Elisha. "British soldiers fired on

the people and left dead bodies in the street. I saw it myself."

"Now, Elisha, there's more to it than that. I saw it too," said Jonny.

"Are you serious?" asked Uncle Nehemiah. "Do you mean those British troops actually fired on the people of Boston?" He rose and stood, white-haired and commanding, his face red with anger. "They wouldn't dare!"

"They did dare," said Elisha. "I was walking down King Street by the Custom House listening to some fracas between a child and a British Captain who was refusing to pay a debt or something of the sort when I saw the sentry, Montgomery his name is, threaten to blow the brains out of a black man named Crispus Attucks. Then he called the guards, and Captain Preston and some others came out and the Captain told the men to prime and load, and the next thing I knew, me staying back against the wall to keep from getting my own brains blown out, they did fire. There's four men dead, and Captain Preston and his eight lobsterbacks are locked up in the jail."

"And the more's the pity for that," said Jonny. "I saw a thing or two myself. They plagued the sentry until he had to fire or get killed himself. I even saw Attucks take a club and threaten to kill the sentry, and there were only eight British against that countless mob. I tell you, I was not proud of the people of Boston. Of course, they hate having the British troops there, but they're just men like the rest of us, half hungry and homesick for London and always met with sneers and snowballs. I see them from the window where we apprentices eat. Sometimes I have been moved to give one of the poor devils crusts of my own bread."

"You are like your father, Jonny, always kind to the other side," said Mother.

"There are two sides, all right," said Jonny. "I don't like the way Parliament is treating us here, but that's no reason to harass these soldiers. 'Taint their fault they're here."

Deborah felt her blood run with excitement. How starved she had been, stuck in the quiet kitchen in Middleborough. The Boston Massacre they called it later, even when Captain Preston and his men were cleared of the murder charge with Mr. John Adams as their lawyer.

Deborah didn't forget it. Who could forget anything as stirring as the news that always spilled out of Boston town. Someday she would get there herself. She told Jonny so.

"You get to Boston?" Jonny laughed and pulled her braid playfully.

"What would a single, lone, little girl like you do in Boston town? Na, Deb, be content with your kitchen."

"Boston is no place for a decent woman these days. They say the British soldiers rob the women on the streets," said Elisha. "Last night I heard a woman got her muff, bonnet, and tippet lifted from her."

"Nobody would do that to me," said Deborah

defiantly. "I'd fight them off if I had such a fine outfit."

"I believe you," laughed Jonny, "but you're lucky to be in safe little Middleborough now."

Deborah reluctantly returned to Middleborough in a week. Poor Madam Thacher was so ill and old that there was no companionship in looking after her, only hard work. Zillah, fat, lazy, and unloved as ever, was jealous of Deborah's holiday and harassed her more than before. Deborah kept her mouth shut in a firm line, her face impassive, determined never to show Zillah the anger that seethed within her.

Zillah, like a stupid child poking at a caged snake, picked at Deborah, trying to break the aloof reserve into a fit of ordinary temper. Deborah kept her steely resistance tight about herself, offering no cracks on her calm surface. But there were ways to fight back.

"Empty the slops," ordered Zillah one day.

Deborah silently picked up the slop bucket and very carefully walked close to Zillah, spilling part of the brimming bucket on Zillah's skirt. Zillah shrieked.

"Forgive me," said Deborah, excessively polite. "Let me wash it off for you."

"No, no," fumed Zillah. "Leave me be, you clumsy brat."

That night when Deborah looked for her precious book it was missing from under her pillow. Of course

Zillah had taken it, for she was sitting close to the home fire for a change, watching Deborah. I won't give her the satisfaction of noticing, decided Deborah grimly, taking another book from the shelf instead.

The next day she found her book hidden under the eaves in the attic. She in turn hid it behind the Bible on the shelf. Zillah would never find it there.

But Zillah did find it. In the summer days while Deborah worked in the garden behind the house the book was hidden and found many times with nothing said.

Madam Thacher was chiefly bedridden now, and each day Deborah must read aloud to her for many hours. The old lady had taken a great fancy to the Book of Numbers. Deborah, weary of the ceaseless lists of names, would sometimes substitute the stories of Gulliver in a low singsong when Madam Thacher nodded off in one of her frequent naps.

Zillah sometimes listened with feigned indifference as Deborah read of magic kingdoms and Lilliputians, and the book was not hidden any more. But one day in December, the day before Deborah's tenth birthday, Zillah was put in an especially bad temper. Madam Thacher, her mind sharper than usual, had kept Deborah at her reading most of the day. Toward evening, she peremptorily ordered Zillah to bring in wood and carry out ashes herself to leave Deborah free to read.

Then Madam Thacher fell asleep, and Zillah returned to the kitchen, half frozen, to see Deborah snugly ensconced in a chair, happily reading her book to herself while the old lady snored.

"So," said Zillah. "I think I have found a way to fix you, miss. I shall go to the good Mr. Conant who favors you so highly with the gift of a worldly book and tell him how you use it to deceive the old lady, mumbling from that heathen book when she thinks you are reading from the Holy Scripture. Then we'll see what happens to the prized book!"

Deborah put the book down, feeling the blood rise to her face. It was rather mean to deceive Madam Thacher, but then she didn't comprehend what was read when she was half asleep. It was only the sound of a voice that she needed. That night Deborah foolishly laid Gulliver on the mantel alongside the Bible. The next morning it was gone.

"If you're looking for your book, I have taken it to Mr. Conant. You won't see it again," said Zillah nastily.

Perhaps it was because it was her forgotten birthday. Perhaps it was the cruelly cold weather, the sheer boredom of her tiresome life, or homesickness, or the endless pettiness of Zillah, but most of all it was the fear that Zillah had actually taken the book to Mr. Conant. Deborah broke, losing her head so completely that she did not stop to realize that Zillah could not possibly have taken the book away at that hour of the morning.

She screamed at Zillah, and grabbing her worn cloak from the hook by the door she ran out into the deep snow, tears running down her cheeks, her hair disheveled, and anger tearing her with fierce intensity.

Down the road to Mr. Conant's house she staggered, falling into deep drifts, pulling herself out again, crying out with shuddering sobs that shook her frame. Nothing in her life had ever equaled her rage.

She hurled herself at Mr. Conant's kitchen door. The servant woman was blowing up the fire for breakfast when the hysterical Deborah flung herself into the room.

"I—I—did she—did she—?" cried Deborah incoherently.

"Sakes alive, 'tis the child from Madam Thacher's. She's having a fit!" shouted the woman.

Deborah fell onto the settle, bent double, with only her back showing her convulsive trembling.

"I pray God will punish her," she cried out to the astonished Mr. Conant, who had rushed into the room. "She gave you back my book!"

The woman and Mr. Conant raised Deborah's head and wiped her face, and Deborah became a little calmer. Finally, forcing a spoon of warm tea between her lips, they stopped her tears entirely. Deborah gave a deep sigh and fell limply back onto the pillow Mr. Conant had slipped behind her back.

"Did Zillah give you my book?" she asked dully, looking pleadingly at Mr. Conant. The minister looked uncomprehendingly back at her. Then Deborah knew how silly she had been to believe that Zillah had really done it; but now she was here, cold, hungry, and wretched.

She broke down, giving Mr. Conant the whole torrential story of the book, of Zillah's constant meanness, of her trials with the old lady, and her longing for escape.

Mr. Conant listened with concern. He nodded to the woman, who was cooking bacon and corncakes, motioning her to bring Deborah some food.

"Something will be done," he promised. "But first ask a merciful God to forgive you for praying a curse on Zillah."

"Yes, sir," said Deborah meekly.

" 'What is a dutiful child's promise?' " he asked her.

" 'I will forgive my enemies and pray to God for them,' " quoted Deborah, recalling her Catechism.

"Very good. I have been troubled by your state. I even had a letter from your mother asking if another place could be found for you. She fears the work is too heavy for you at Madam Thacher's. I think the time has come for Madam Thacher to give up that house and go live with other relatives who can care for her better than the foolish Zillah."

"Where will I go?" asked Deborah in alarm. "Please sir, do not trouble my mother. She has enough worries now. I can make my peace with Zillah."

"But things are already acting in your behalf, Deborah. Deacon Thomas, who took you to Plymouth last spring, is looking for a young woman to help his wife. If I can persuade them that you are not too young, this might be a solution for you."

Deborah sat up, her face alight. "Oh, I would love to help that pretty Mistress Thomas and all those lively little boys. I would work twice as hard as anybody else, I promise."

"I believe you," said Mr. Conant. "Now eat your breakfast and stay here until I return."

IV

1771–1773: The Boston Tea Party took place in 1773.

Deborah, with her precious book and her few clothes, arrived at the Thomas house two days later. It was agreed that she was to stay for ten years to work in exchange for food, clothing, and shelter.

She was so happy to part with Zillah that she gave her a warm good-by, and Zillah, glad to be rid of her irksome job, was polite to Deborah at the last. Poor Madam Thacher was hardly conscious of the change.

Deborah kissed her on the cheek. She had always been kind, and Deborah had in turn been kind to her. Parting is easier if there are no regrets on the conscience, Deborah decided.

Mr. Conant took Deborah to the Thomas farm in his sleigh. Mistress Thomas opened the kitchen door and welcomed them, brushing three little boys out of the way so Mr. Conant and Deborah could warm themselves by the fire.

"You, Ransom, you, Jeremiah, take Deborah's bundle to the loft room where she is to sleep," said Mistress Thomas to the two oldest boys, who looked to be about six and eight.

Deborah sat on the edge of the settle and looked around the cozy kitchen. The smallest boy, a redhead, sidled up to her, reached out his finger and touched her quickly, and then ran giggling back to the corner of the room.

"You, Silas, haven't you ever seen a girl before? Come back here and make your manners to Mr. Conant. He's only four. He hardly ever sees anyone out here on the farm," said his mother.

A baby cry came from the cradle beside Mistress Thomas. She leaned over and picked up a red-faced baby, struggling with the layers of cloth wrapped about him.

"This is Abraham. He's a year old and too big for the cradle, but he screams when I put him in the standing stool. He wants to walk, and he will when I get these swaddles off him."

"I'll watch him," said Deborah eagerly. "I'll see that he gets into no trouble."

"Don't make a promise you can't keep," said Mistress Thomas. "You don't know the Thomas boys. Hold the baby, Deborah, while I make us some tea. Mr. Thomas tells me there won't be much more tea drinking in the colonies. Did you hear of a new society being formed here with the members promising not to drink tea? It makes no sense to me."

"I did hear such," said Mr. Conant. "In fact, I am a member. The sense is that Parliament, for all they repealed the Stamp Act, imposed a new tax on tea. Men with brains in Boston say we should not give in. If they tax tea and we agree to it by buying the taxed tea, then they will tax everything. But I confess this old untaxed tea will taste very good right now, and we will miss our cups of tea."

"What will we drink when we don't have tea?" asked Deborah.

"We'll use herbs," said Mistress Thomas placidly. "There's sassafras and Indian root, and I've even tried a brew made of burnt sweet potatoes, but 'tis a poor drink."

That night Deborah snuggled under the covers in the loft room over the kitchen. It was warm from the kitchen fireplace, and Mistress Thomas gave her her own candle. Never in her life had she slept in a room alone. Only the very rich or a poor outcast like herself had the luxury of privacy.

Poor outcast? That was hardly the word. She was

tingling with the good cheer of the house, the hearty food on the table, and the enthusiastic delight of the boys in the stories she told them after she had finished helping Mistress with the dishes. It was a good world to go to sleep in here under the eaves with her warm cover and her warm welcome.

When she awoke the next morning, a dim light came through the floor opening, and a gray line marked the window shutter. Everything was quiet, only the creaking of the white-oak house timbers and the sound of the winter winds and pelts of snow broke the silence. Deborah snuggled half awake under her covers. She was pulled abruptly from her lethargy with a scream from below. The hubbub that followed got Deborah onto her feet and into her clothes and down the ladder in seconds.

In the cold kitchen, in the middle of a pool of clabbered milk, sat Abraham, shrieking. Deacon and Mistress Thomas in wrappers and the boys in their drawers and undershirts were dancing around the yelling baby and the spilled milk in mass confusion.

"I'll take Abraham," cried Deborah, reaching for the soggy baby while Mistress Thomas and Ransom wiped up the spreading circle of milk. Silas and Jeremiah picked up the overturned churn. While the Deacon blew up the fire, Deborah sponged the wriggling Abraham and dressed him in the clothes that Mistress Thomas handed to her.

"I tell you, Mr. Thomas, you've got to make a new bed for this child," fumed Mistress.

"I can't make a new bed in a day, even though a baby can grow from an infant to a child overnight. He must be taught to stay in the cradle," said the Deacon.

"Taught, faugh!" said Mistress Thomas scathingly. "You take on the job of teaching him not to crawl out of his cradle to overturn the churn."

Deborah, pacifying Abraham with spoons of milk from the pitcher on the table, looked at the cradle.

"Mistress, I believe we could change the cradle about so that he could not get out," said Deborah. "If the rockers could be unjoined and turned upside down to keep the cradle steady and a few slats were nailed to the sides, I believe we could make a cage-like bed that would keep him safe when our backs are turned."

The Deacon picked up the cradle and examined the rockers. "I believe it would work," he said. "You have a good head, Deborah. I can do it within the hour."

The day rushed forward as busily as it began. Deborah gathered eggs with Jeremiah, she brought in wood with Ransom, she rescued Silas from the fire where he was playing with forbidden blazing sticks. She kneaded the bread for Mistress, she swept the floor and shook the hearthrug, and she helped Ransom carry the huge bucket of ashes to the pit behind the barn. She found herself singing with Mistress, who was happy at her work.

She scrubbed a peck of potatoes from the root cellar and laid them in the ashes. She stirred the soup; she washed Abraham's diapers and hung them by the fire. When she offered to help Ransom and Jeremiah bring in the kitchen water from the well, Mistress Thomas put a kindly restraining hand on her shoulder.

"Gracious, child, don't burn yourself out the first day. Sit and rest a mite. For all you're bound over to us, you're no slave. Have you a sampler or needlework?"

Deborah shook her head. "I have not worked a sampler since Cousin Fuller died. I have almost forgotten my stitches."

"The more's the pity for that," said Mistress Thomas. "I shall find you a square of linen and some stitching thread in a day or two. Meantime, have you nought but that black dress to wear?"

Deborah shook her head. "Just this and another one like it, except the other one is too small. This was my sister Hannah's. Because our father died and Cousin Fuller died, I had to wear black, and I had no money for other clothes."

"That's all right. I'm not reproaching you. I only asked because I have a dress that I wore before these boy babies stretched me out of shape. I can never wear it again, and since it seems that God only sends me boys I'll give that dress to you, as I have no girl child to pass it on to. Run look in the press in my sleeping room, and, toward the back, behind my maroon silk, you'll find a striped wool dress."

"Oh, Mistress," cried Deborah when she returned with the dress over her arm, "surely you wouldn't part with it."

"Yes, surely I would," said Mistress Thomas. "I

can't bear to see a child in my kitchen in black now." She drew Deborah onto the settle and leaned confidentially toward her.

"I've a mind to tell you a secret that has not even been spoken to Deacon Thomas yet. I can't have a person in mourning around me all day now because it might mark my unborn child. There now, you have the first news of it. I think I will be having a new baby come September or October, and I know that I shall never get my fat waist into that garment again."

"Oh, Mistress Thomas, how I will work to help you! I shall be its nurse. What can I fetch you?"

"Nothing," laughed Mistress Thomas. "But perhaps by giving away this dress I will get a girl this time. Here, take off your black dress and see how this fits. Why, it won't need much taking up, just here and here. Run fetch my sewing basket, and we'll fix it now."

"It's the most beautiful dress I ever saw," exclaimed Deborah, looking down at herself in the cream and indigo striped wool dress.

"I dyed, spun, and wove the wool for it myself when Mr. Thomas was courting me," said Mistress. "Here, tuck your kerchief in here to make the neck warmer, and always keep your linen apron over it to keep it clean, and it will do you nicely for the winter. Oh, I wish I were young and pretty again."

"But Mistress, you *are* young and pretty," protested Deborah.

"Young, my foot. I'm twenty-nine years old. Nobody is pretty after four children in nine years. But my teeth aren't gone as bad as some. I've lost two in all, but most women lose a tooth for a child. Oh, how I like having a girl about the house. You seem uncommonly old for a child. I live out here with only males. The cows and I are the only females on the place."

"Don't forget the hens," giggled Deborah. For the first time in her life she was consciously proud of being a female. It was good to be a girl in a pretty dress, to share the confidences of a kind and happy woman. She went to the loft and found the scrap of comb that Cousin Fuller had given her.

"Mistress, mayhap you have a looking glass?" she asked timidly.

"On the cupboard door," said Mistress Thomas. "Fluff your hair out a bit and sit beside me. I will set you to darning while Abraham is still asleep. And that reminds me that we'll be having new shoes made for you when the shoemaker comes around to make shoes for the boys." Deborah glanced with embarrassment at her dirty, torn, Indian moccasins.

Deborah combed her hair and washed her face and, tucking her kerchief around the neck of her new dress and tying the apron over it, she sat down beside her new mistress feeling and looking like a new girl.

Days were so busy that it was spring before Deborah could believe it. Abraham was into everything except

71

when they put him, protesting, into his cage. Most nights Deborah would gather the three older boys about her and teach them their letters. She rewarded them with episodes from GULLIVER'S TRAVELS while Mistress Thomas rocked the rambunctious Abraham.

"It shames me that I have not sent them to school more. This summer we shall send Silas and Jeremiah to the dame school, and in the winter Ransom shall go to the town school. Deacon will have to start cutting wood for Ransom's share. To be honest, I am not much of a reader myself, and Mr. Thomas is not as much of a hand with books as he is with farming."

"I like teaching them," said Deborah.

"We must get on with the Catechisms. When I was a lass, every little child had to know the SPIRITUAL MILK for the tithing man, or its parents would answer for it. I would not like to tell Deacon Thomas this, for he is very straight about such matters, but I hated learning the Catechism. I must not fail my children though. They will learn it or get the stick from their father."

"Do you know the Elder Backus?" asked Deborah, who was knitting by the door.

"Everybody in Middleborough knows him," said Mistress, reaching out to catch Abraham, who was scampering out the door after Silas. "He's a Baptist and holds with some strange ideas. But he is a good man for all that."

"I used to see him often when I looked out the window at Madam Thacher's. He doesn't believe that there should be a church tax to pay the town minister. He thinks a person should pay his church money where he goes to church. I heard there was a widow named Madam Kimball over at Bradford who said she wouldn't pay her church tax because she was a Baptist, and she got dragged out of her house one night. Mr. Backus got so mad he wrote letters to the Boston newspapers about it. I think the woman had her rights."

"That's crazy talk, Deborah. The world is full of zanies, and I thank God I'm not one of them. Not pay the ministerial fee indeed. What will the world come to if we don't do things the way our parents did?"

"It might improve," said Deborah tentatively.

"Don't let Deacon Thomas hear any of that kind of talk from you, miss," said Mistress sternly. "I'm ashamed of you."

"Mistress, since this is the first pleasant night of spring, could I take the boys to the sheltered place by the barn and tell them a Bible story instead of studying the Catechism?"

"I can't see the harm," said Mistress Thomas. This child was a jewel despite the strange ideas that sometimes popped out of her. And she was growing so. "Deborah, child," she added, "when the peddler man comes I will get you a few yards of muslin for a summer dress. It will soon be too hot for linsey-woolsey and that leather bodice."

"Oh, thank you, Mistress," cried Deborah. She took Abraham by the hand and called to the other boys. "I'm

73

going to tell you about the woman warrior instead of hearing your Catechism tonight."

Ransom and Jeremiah ended their game of stone poison tag and ran across the grass to Deborah, who had scooped Abraham into her lap and squeezed Silas beside her.

"You mean Mam says we don't have to study the Catechism tonight?" said Jeremiah unbelievingly.

"That's right," said Deborah. "I'm going to tell you a Bible story instead, one that Cousin Fuller used to tell me when I was about the size of Silas."

"Tell us about the little people in your book instead," suggested Ransom. "Mam won't know the difference."

"I'll know the difference," said Deborah scathingly. "Tonight I am Judge Deborah, and you will find out who I really am. I was named for the woman warrior."

"That's a lie," said Ransom. "You were named for your mother. I heard Mam say so."

"Do you want to hear the story?" asked Deborah coolly.

"Yuh, I want to hear the story," said Ransom. This girl was more like a grown person, but his father had told him that Deborah was not even eleven yet.

"Once there was a beautiful and witty woman named Deborah. She was a judge over all Israel."

"That's wrong," said Jeremiah. "Only men can be judges."

"You're wrong," said Deborah. "It's in the Book of

74

Judges in the Bible that she was a judge and sat under a palm tree in the country of Ephraim. My brother Ephraim is named for that. All the people came to her for judgment."

"They came to a *woman?*" asked Ransom, incredulous.

"Yes, and then she sent for Barak, the general of the Israelite Army, and told him that the Lord said for him to get ten thousand soldiers and follow him and to go out and fight Sisera, the general of the king of Canaan. They were enemies, you see."

"I like it about wars," said Silas.

"This General Sisera had nine hundred chariots of iron," continued Deborah, her eyes glistening at the thought of it. "Imagine nine hundred chariots riding down the road here. Why, they would reach all the way to Middleborough and then some."

"Wow," said Jeremiah.

"And this General did everything Deborah commanded him to do," said Deborah.

"I don't think any general would do that," objected Ransom.

"This one did. In fact, he said he would not fight unless Deborah went with him."

"Was this really you, Deborah?" asked Silas, puzzled.

"Of course not, you stupid," said Jeremiah. "It's some old tale. I don't believe it for one minute."

"Judge Deborah told General Barak that if she

went with him, a woman would get the credit, but he didn't care. So with Deborah by his side Barak beat all the soldiers of Sisera with their nine hunderd chariots of iron and killed them every one except General Sisera, and he ran away."

"He was afraid of Deborah," said Silas, his eyes big.

"He was afraid of Deborah, and he was tired. Guess what he did?" said Deborah dramatically.

"I don't know," breathed Ransom. "I must not have listened if they told this story in church."

"There was a woman named Jael, and her husband was supposed to be a friend of General Sisera. And Jael saw General Sisera coming up the road and she went outside her tent. The people all lived in tents like the Indians up at Neponset, and she told him to come in and take a rest and she would guard him. Do you know what my great-grandmother's name was?" she asked importantly.

"No, but don't stop the story," begged Ransom.

"Her name was Jael too. My great-grandmother was named Jael Hobart Bradford, and she was named for this Jael out of the Bible too."

"Zounds!" said Ransom.

"I'll tell on you for swearing, Ransom Thomas," said Jeremiah righteously.

"Zounds!" said Ransom again.

"Well, this Jael in the Bible invited General Sisera in and he went to sleep, and when he was snoring pretty hard Jael took a tent peg and a hammer. General Sisera was lying on the ground like this." She pushed Silas' head to the ground so that his temple lay under her finger. "Then she took the tent peg and she hammered his head down to the ground fast and killed him dead."

"Oh, how mean of her," said Silas, rubbing his temple.

"It was mean, but it was war. That's how they did it in Old Testament days. I daresay he deserved it, but I think he got cheated. Jael deceived him. Then Deborah sang a song about what had happened and thanked God that women had triumphed over the enemy."

"Deborah, you tell the best stories," said Jeremiah.

"Some day I shall tell you about the Maid of Orleans who put on breeches and led the French Army into battle."

"I know I won't believe that story," said Ransom stoutly. "No woman has ever put on breeches. If she did they'd run her out of town."

"They did worse than that to Joan," said Deborah. "They burned her to death for it."

In June, Jeremiah and Silas went to school. Deborah forced down her envy. There were a few girls in the school. They went early in the morning from six-thirty to nine and again late in the afternoon.

"Why can't Deborah go to school with the girls?" asked Jeremiah.

"We can't spare her now," said Deacon Thomas. "Besides, I think she reads better than the teacher."

Every day, Deborah made Jeremiah show her what he had learned. What had his teacher said? How was the letter formed? What did the number mean? At night after everyone was in bed she secretly copied from Jeremiah's book, perfecting her own writing by candlelight, on birch bark, using a goose quill and home-made ink. Nobody had taught her much about writing. She must teach herself if she wanted to learn.

She studied the sky at night and bombarded the Deacon with questions. With his farmer's eye he knew about the heavens. While Ransom and Jeremiah listened too, the Deacon explained the solar system, how the earth went around the sun and how the moon circled the earth.

"I wish I owned a geography book," said Deborah.

"It gives girls the brain fever to study too much," said the Deacon sternly. "Put your thoughts on the kitchen and dairy, miss. It's what we eat and wear that counts. Leave the deep matters to God and your betters."

Deborah rose with the meadow larks in the morning and ran barefoot in the fields, digging the garden, borning the lambs, milking, tending the chickens. But Sundays were dreary with long hours of church and nothing to do, no games, no running, no reading except the Bible, no sewing. Deacon Thomas even insisted that the milking must be done and the cows put to pasture before sunup and not brought in until after dark. The pigs and sheep could not roam, and Deborah thought, secretly smiling, he would stop the cock from crowing if he could.

"Please, sir, could I go into the woods and meditate?" Deborah asked the Deacon.

"Let her," said Mistress Thomas, swiftly coming to Deborah's aid.

"I suppose there is no harm if you meditate on divine matters," said the Deacon reluctantly.

Deborah found herself a wonderful hide-out inside a curious pile of rocks. This was her secret eyrie where she spent her Sunday afternoons, not even letting Ransom know about it.

One morning in September, with Abraham at her heels, she was picking cucumbers for pickling when Mistress Thomas called urgently from the back door.

"Deborah, run and call Deacon Thomas to fetch the midwife."

Deborah snatched Abraham in her arms and ran to the upper field for Deacon Thomas. She loaded the children into the cart and took them to their aunt's for the day. When Deacon Thomas galloped in on his horse that afternoon with the news that they had a girl at their house, the rejoicing was contagious.

That night, when they had all seen the tiny red-faced girl, Elizabeth, Deborah took Abraham and Silas with her to the loft room to sleep. Deborah caught sight of the indigo-striped dress that Mistress had given her. It had brought them a girl, just as she predicted, and Elizabeth thrived as all the other Thomas children did.

One winter afternoon while Ransom was at school and Mistress and the baby were away at a quilting and the Deacon and Jeremiah were working at a neighbor's barn, Deborah was left at home with Silas and Abraham. Deborah, in a rare moment of leisure, was working at the kitchen table practicing writing on birch bark when Mr. Conant knocked on the kitchen door.

"I have come to tell you that old Madam Thacher is dead," he said. "What have we here?" he asked, looking at Deborah's makeshift schoolwork.

Deborah reddened. "It's nothing, only some foolishness of mine to better my writing. Deacon Thomas thinks little of women's learning."

" 'Tis not foolishness. I see no reason for girls not to be educated the same as boys, but I know it is impossible for you to go to school with no father to pay your way. I think you show good ambition to try to learn alone."

"I learn by asking and listening," said Deborah. "Every night I ask Jeremiah what he learned in school. It helps him to repeat it, and it is almost as good as going to school myself. If only I had a copybook with some well-formed letters written across the top, I could do as well as those at school. I have learned to figure and cipher and do sums just by using my fingers and thinking."

"Good for you, my girl. I shall bring you a copybook that will be a commonplace book as well. You shall do what is the fashion now and keep one page for good deeds and one page for bad deeds to be a check and balance on your character. If your writing becomes good enough, perhaps you can have a correspondence with another young lady."

"I should never have the paper for such. Even my mother and I print on birch bark when we write, which is seldom enough. Nobody else would use such humble materials."

"Perhaps it will be provided," said Mr. Conant, rising to go. "Give my best regards to your master and mistress. We will meet at the funeral."

Deborah felt a lump in her throat when the church bell tolled the six strokes for a woman and then eighty-four echoing knells for each year of Madam Thacher's life.

Mr. Conant sent Deborah a paper book with letters lined across the top. Deborah copied a line each night, writing very small to make the paper last. The second part of the book had pages labeled *bad* and *good*.

She lay in her bed under the eaves, biting the end of her penstaff each night, writing a laborious list of her sins on the black-mark pages.

. . . Did linger too long at Sproat's Tavern whither I had gone to deliver eggs for my master. Did listen through the kitchen wall to men's political talk in the tap room.

. . . Did run wild on Guy Fawkes Day taking Ransom and Jeremiah with me to the bonfire. Did receive a tongue blistering from Mistress when I returned late with a torn dress.

. . . Did lock Ransom in the outhouse for being uppity to me because I am a girl.

. . . Did shake Abraham until he screamed because he hit Elizabeth with his carved stick.

. . . Did suffer pangs of jealousy when I met a girl from Boston named Mary Morris who is visiting Mistress Bourne. She is proud and no doubt thought me a bumpkin.

. . . The famous Dr. Benjamin Franklin is visiting Judge Oliver. Using the delivery of eggs as an excuse I neglected my chores here to hang around the tavern listening. He told how to make a better horse trough and how a corn broom is better than a birch broom. My hard heart is not sorry I sinned this time. I am only sorry I failed to get one of the Poor Richard papers he was passing out to the men.

. . . Did think profane thoughts on the Sabbath.

In the fall of her twelfth year, Mr. Conant found her a correspondent. Deborah was leaving church with the Thomases when Mr. Conant pulled a sheaf of papers from under his black robe.

"Writing paper for you," he said. "Miss Mary Morris of Boston desires you for a correspondent, and her aunt thinks you would be a good influence for her. Mary is an orphan like you, but luckily she is a rich one."

Deborah thought guiltily of the entry in her copybook as she thanked the minister. Mistress Thomas encouraged the correspondence, as it might make up in a measure for not having Deborah go to school. Deborah sat at the kitchen table with her blank paper before her. "What shall I write?"

"Tell her about the cloth you are weaving," said Mistress.

"Tell her about your flock of lambs," advised Ransom.

"Tell her about the dream you had," said Silas.

"Tell her about me," said Abraham with the vanity of a four-year-old.

In the end, Deborah wrote about her flock. The Deacon had allowed Deborah a portion of the flax field she had harvested, then hatcheled, spun, and woven into linen cloth of such good quality that she sold the piece to Mistress Leonard. With the money she had bought herself a sheep. The Deacon was so impressed with Deborah's enterprise that he gave her a mate to the sheep so that she might begin her own flock.

Deborah took the letter about the flock to Sproat's Tavern and left it for the post rider to Boston. Mary had agreed that she would pay the postage upon receipt.

In December the rider brought Deborah a reply. Mary had no undertaking of her own to report, but she listed that she had a new paste comb, black mitts, and feathers for her hair to match her new watered-silk dress. There were street lights in Boston outside her house, she wrote.

Then she added in a postscript that the people of Boston vere very angry that Governor Hutchinson's sons were determined to receive the tea that was headed for Boston. She, Mary, would be very glad to have some decent tea.

"I myself am sick to death of this patriotic herb tea," said Mistress Thomas with unusual discontent in her voice. "For years I have not had a decent cup of tea without my conscience hurting me." She reached out a protective hand to keep Elizabeth from the fire. She gave the beguilingly blond Elizabeth a smack on the seat. Elizabeth yelled.

Deborah looked up from her letter in surprise. Mistress was never short with the baby and seldom out of sorts with anyone.

"Patience, patience," said the Deacon, reaching over to take Elizabeth onto his knee. "We will not drink their tea. England has gone too far. They say at the tavern that England is sending many shiploads of tea to America and that we will be forced to pay the tax because Boston has been smuggling Dutch tea. The Governor says it *will* be unloaded, the people say it will *not*. They are having open and angry meetings about it, encouraged by Mr. Sam Adams and others. The people are stirred to a frenzy."

The next morning the Deacon went to town for the latest news. "The first tea ship is in Boston Harbor," cried Deacon Thomas, bursting into the kitchen. "The shipmaster has been warned not to unload. Last night a rider came through here on his way to Providence and New Bedford to warn them not to unload the ships if they go there."

Mistress Thomas sat down on the settle and burst into tears.

"Oh, Mistress," cried Deborah, her mouth and eyes wide with interest, "whatever is the matter? I never guessed you cared so much about the tea ships."

" 'Tis not the tea ships," she sobbed. "I care and know nought about such. But 'tis time you all knew that

I am with child again and my breakfast sits poorly in my belly."

On her thirteenth birthday, December 17, 1773, Deborah was awakened by a great banging on the kitchen door. She flung on her clothes and hurried down, but Deacon Thomas had already opened the door and admitted the neighbor from the next farm.

"They dumped the tea," he cried, stamping the snow from his feet.

"Who did? How?" cried Deacon Thomas. Deborah listened avidly.

"Some hardy souls in Boston. Hundreds of them dressed up like Indians and went aboard the three ships and dumped the whole cargo into the harbor. That'll teach Parliament how we make salt-water tea in Massachusetts."

Deacon Thomas dressed, ate a hurried cold breakfast, and followed his neighbor to the tavern.

"I'm coming too," shouted Ransom.

Deborah watched enviously as they strode away. Being a girl, she turned from the window and made breakfast for the children. She sighed. The months would be hard ones with Mistress in the family way again. She snatched Elizabeth from the hearth and handed Abraham a slice of venison. Tea dumping or not, there was work to be done, and the milking would fall to her this morning.

Zounds! said Deborah wickedly to herself. How I wish I could have been there. All I'm good for is a kitchen slave. Involuntarily she glanced out the window, and thought of Mother and Grandmère.

I'd better forget about myself this morning, she told herself grimly. I'll just think about that tea party in Boston.

V

1774–1777: In 1774 the Port of Boston was closed, and the First Continental Congress met in Philadelphia.

The Battle of Lexington and the Battle of Bunker Hill took place in 1775.

The Declaration of Independence was signed in 1776.

Burgoyne surrendered to the Americans at Saratoga in 1777.

In May, Jacob Thomas was born. Deborah was so busy taking care of the children during Mistress' recovery that she hardly had time to keep up with the stirring news.

Boston was going to be punished for dumping the tea, she found out as she rocked baby Jacob and listened to the neighbors who came in to see the new baby. On the first of June the port would be closed until the

87

town paid for the tea. The Crown appointed General Gage as Governor, and more British troops were due at any moment to maintain order. From now on, Salem would be the capital of Massachusetts Colony.

"Boston will starve," declared Deacon Thomas at the dinner table. Elizabeth overturned the milk pitcher.

"I've no time for hearing of such matters," said Mistress. "Abraham, come wipe up the milk from the floor, and you, Silas, go fetch more from the milk room."

But Deborah thought long on it. That night she used one of her last pieces of paper to write to Mary in Boston to ask for the news. Mary had left Boston, Deborah found out much later, for she never had a reply to the letter. She had gone away to Nova Scotia with relatives. Many people who liked bread and butter better than politics and principles were leaving Boston now.

Deborah walked to Sproat's Tavern and saw the broadside of the Boston Port Bill posted on the door. Someone had printed it with a skull and crossbones and mourning bands. The King and Parliament were out to kill Boston, thought Deborah indignantly. I wish I could help stop them.

"There'll be starvation in Boston next winter," said Mr. Conant grimly as he stopped to speak to Deborah. "I'm suggesting that each person should plant extra grain for our Boston neighbors. They'll need it."

"I'll help," said Deborah eagerly. "Deacon Thomas is generous with his land. Ransom and Jeremiah and I can put in an extra acre of corn. It's not too late to plant. We'll begin this very day."

"Deborah, Deborah, you were formed for enterprise," said Mr. Conant. "This has been said about you before."

Middleborough sent eighty bushels of grain to the beleaguered Boston in October, adding its offering to those that poured in from the other colonies. Deborah, Ransom, and Jeremiah saw the sacks of grain being stacked on the carts with theirs among the rest. Deborah felt she had made her first stake for liberty. How I would love to stow away in a bag of grain and go to Boston to see the famous streets, she thought dreamily, but of course such thoughts must be kept to herself.

The First Continental Congress was meeting down in Philadelphia now, they said. What was Philadelphia like? Deborah tried hard to imagine a city ten or a hundred or a thousand times as big as Middleborough.

But in little Middleborough, Captain William Shaw began training his company of soldiers. They called them minutemen because, they whispered, they must be ready for anything at a minute's notice. Deborah watched them drill on the Lower Green, where she loitered one afternoon returning from an errand for Mistress. Mother had written that Jonny was drilling up in Concord, where he lived now, and Elisha, his ship idle in Salem Harbor, was probably in a company too. Even Eph, now sixteen, might be trying his best to get a powder horn and a gun with a bayonet.

The Thomas boys played soldier behind the barn with sticks over their shoulders while Deborah and Mistress spun and wove ceaselessly. With the port closed, there was no more imported dye. Deborah and Jeremiah gathered pokeberries to mix with alum for making red dye to use instead of the customary indigo blue. They dyed it in the wool, experimenting with lovely red yarns.

Some days they swapped work with neighbors. Deborah loved these sociable occasions. Spinning six skeins of wool was a good day's work for a woman, and as Deborah could almost equal that, she was always invited to go with Mistress.

"My feet won't carry me far enough for fast wool spinning," said Mistress. "I think a spinner must walk nearly twenty miles a day, back and forth with the yarn."

On Deborah's fourteenth birthday, she and Mistress were set up for a rag rug making when a neighbor came in with news.

"What a lot I have to tell you," exclaimed Mistress Bennett as she took off her cloak and drew up to the fire. "Some Patriots up at Portsmouth in New Hampshire got word that the British troops were going to seize the powder at Fort William and Mary, so they went in first and made the British garrison surrender and took the guns and nigh a hundred kegs of powder and loaded it on a boat in the river and hid it. The men were almost frozen from wading the stream, but they thought it would be wise for the Colonists to have the arms instead of the British. They whisper it that the British want to seize all the arms in Massachusetts."

"How brave! How did they ever keep from freezing in that water? Where did they hide the guns and powder?" exclaimed Deborah.

"I can't answer your questions, but I know it's a fact they did it," said Mistress Bennett.

"I wish it were hidden here," said Deborah vehemently. "I'd help guard it."

"Hardly women's work," said Mistress Bennett tartly.

In April, 1775, the prediction about the British and the gunpowder came true. Deborah was in the barn with Ransom sorting out flax seed when Jeremiah came dashing in.

"Where's Father? The Regulars have fired on the Colonists. Caleb Bryant told Thomas Ellis, and he's already cleaning his gun, and there's fighting in Lexington and Concord. It's war, they say. War, war, whoopee, bang, bang!" He pranced about, shouting and doing a crazy dance.

Deborah and Ransom dropped the seeds and ran shouting for the Deacon. He hurried away to the town and came back later with the news.

"It's true, all right. There's been open fighting in Lexington and Concord between General Gage's Redcoats and the Massachusetts minutemen. Paul Revere, the silversmith, rode to Lexington to warn the people that the British were coming to get the guns and powder they had hidden there."

The bells of the town were ringing. Deborah stood by the kitchen door and heard the slow steady knelling that marked the death of peace between Britain and her Colony of Massachusetts.

Poor Boston, thought Deborah. The British were

determined to bring her to utter ruin now. "I wish I could have seen that town," she said wistfully to Ransom that evening as they drove the cows in from the pasture for milking.

"Oh, Boston will last," said Ransom airily. "We men will fight for it. I expect I'll be seeing it before too many months go by."

"Listen to the child," said Deborah scornfully. "You're barely thirteen years old."

That night the town was wild with excitement, for three companies of minutemen had marched from Middleborough to Marshfield, up above Plymouth, to suppress Tories to whom British General Gage had sent arms. When the Middleborough men returned victorious in two days, Deborah stood on the roadside and cheered until she cried.

Ransom was a good source of news. Deborah, who had to stay at home in the evenings looking after Elizabeth and Jacob and helping Mistress, envied the fleet-footed freedom of Ransom, who rushed off to the town for news every spring night after supper.

. . . Thirty thousand volunteers from Connecticut are on their way to Boston.

. . . General Gage has tried to dissolve the Massachusetts Assembly in Salem. The messenger was locked out and he read the order on the stairs while the Assembly laughed openly.

. . . Mr. John Hancock, the head of the Assembly, has ordered a day of prayer and fasting that King George will soften his heart to the Colonies.

. . . The Patriots are leaving Boston in droves, and the Loyalists are moving into town.

Deborah saw refugees every day. The roads were clogged with them.

"A fellow named Ethan Allen took the British Fort Ticonderoga and got all the powder for the Americans," cried Ransom, running in one evening from town.

"What do you mean, *British* and *American?*" asked his mother shortly. "We're all British subjects. There's too much talk of fighting a civil war."

"This is no civil war. We have to decide whether we're British or Americans. There's talk of independence everywhere," said Ransom.

"Independence indeed," snorted Mistress Thomas. "This will all be settled soon. Get to your woodwork while there's still light. I need a new bucket for the kitchen."

"But, Mistress, he's right. There's going to be a real war for independence, and I'm for the Americans," said Deborah, her hands in the dishwater. "All those troops camped up there by Boston are ready for a fight. Even Deacon Thomas says so."

"Maybe you're right," sighed Mistress Thomas. "But with five sons that I'm raising to be farmers, I don't relish the war fever that's seizing everybody."

They got their fight. Deborah woke early in the morning on June 17. It was a still, humid day. She had

93

slept badly, had dreamed that she had fought a dragon and won. She lay a moment in her bed thinking of her dream and told it later to Silas as they weeded the bean patch.

At noon, when she sank down under the cool shade of the apple tree and ate the bread and milk she had brought from the kitchen, she thought of the dream again, and the *boom, boom, boom* she heard in the distance seemed part of the dream and part of the pounding blood in her head.

"Do you hear a noise?" she asked Deacon Thomas.

The Deacon listened. "It sounds like heavy gunfire," he said. He put down his mattock. "Happen I have business in the town. I'll find out the news."

The news was that there was bloody fighting on Breed's Hill, or, as some disputed, it was Bunker Hill, in Boston. It was war indeed.

Ransom brought more news.

. . . The Continental Congress was meeting again in Philadelphia and voted to have Continental money.

. . . They're going to start the manufacture of gunpowder over at Stoughton.

. . . George Washington has been made the Commander-in-Chief of the Continental Army.

The British have left Boston was the good news in March, 1776. General Washington had driven them out. Now the refugees were going back to Boston to drive the Tories out.

Some people still didn't know what they were. A

few families were divided down the middle. Many fled to Canada; others stuck it out, trying to keep free of politics and tend their farms.

On May 20, the Deacon came home from town meeting with the great news that Middleborough, like many other townships, had voted for independence if the Continental Congress so decided. Deborah, leaning over the loft opening to hear better, nearly lost her balance in her excitement.

But the greatest news came on July 4, 1776, a few days later. The United States of America was born. The wild ringing of the bells, the shouts, the contagious excitement, brought the whole family in from the fields.

Deacon Thomas put down his tools and hitched up the wagon.

"Wife," he said, "put on your best dress, have Deborah do the same, wash the children, and we are going to town."

Deborah, now a tall slender fifteen, sat between Mistress and Elizabeth. Mistress had given her a looking glass for her birthday, and Deborah had looked at herself approvingly in her blue-sprigged muslin with her hair combed into a single curl over her shoulder.

The noise in town was enough to frighten the little ones. Taking Elizabeth by the hand, Deborah disappeared into the crowd. A fresh boy yanked her curl. Deborah switched her full skirt and flipped her curl back in place.

An informal parade began with every musical instrument in town put to work. Jeremiah found a fife somewhere and pranced into the parade, to the great envy of Ransom, who merely shambled along behind with a great gang of knobby-kneed boys.

Middleborough now had eight military companies. Deborah watched them drill. There was little enough discipline and no uniforms, but they were armed with muskets, home-made bullets, and powder horns.

Outside the tavern stood a post to measure the men who volunteered. One winter morning after Deborah delivered the eggs she stepped outside and, thinking nobody was looking, she backed up to the pole. She carefully held her finger on the mark and turned around to see how tall she was. Five feet six inches! Why, there were many men fighting down in New York and New Jersey with General Washington right now who didn't measure that tall.

"Planning to enlist?" said a voice over her shoulder. Deborah turned to meet the eyes of Jenny, the Negro servant girl who lived at the Leonard's house.

"At least it would get me away from Middleborough for a while," said Deborah. "Everybody's going places—Boston, New York, Rhode Island. Even the Tories are going to Canada. Me, I just stay here and mind the chickens and cows and babies and rake the fields and make the soap and candles and give a hand in the barn."

"Us two, we're servants, Deborah," said Jenny. "That's what we have to do. It could be worse. I have a good mistress and we have good times at our house."

"I have a good mistress too," said Deborah, "but, Jenny, I want to see what it's like out where things are happening."

"War is what is happening out there," said Jenny. "Not for me. I'll stay in Middleborough where the guns are still over the fireplaces most of the time."

"All my old ancestors made the long journey from England," said Deborah. "Even my father went across the ocean, though the sea finally killed him. Whatever the cost, I wish I could go somewhere."

"My ancestors came from Africa," said Jenny, "but that doesn't make me want to go anywhere. Everyone says you're too smart to be a girl. Why don't you get rid of your strange ideas?"

"There's no law against a girl having ideas, I guess," said Deborah. "But I'm restless, I'd better get home before Mistress sends for me."

General Washington won the Battle of Trenton and the Battle of Princeton, and the recruiting men came beating the drum for volunteers. Deborah watched the men and boys march forward and sign their names and receive the bounty money in engraved crisp new Continental bills. The Reverend Mr. Conant was one of the first to go. He signed up as a chaplain and took thirty-five men from the Congregational Church with him.

"Whatever will we do without you?" said Deborah as she told her old friend good-by. "Aren't you, well, you know—" She broke off, embarrassed.

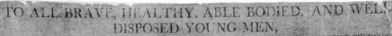

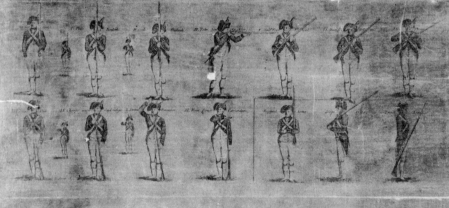

A 1798 recruiting poster.

"You mean am I not a little old for going off to war?" he said with a laugh. "That I am. I'm fifty-seven, but the soldiers need chaplains more than the people here need a minister. Good-by, my girl. I will see you when I return."

But Deborah never saw her friend again. A week before her seventeenth birthday Mr. Conant died of small-pox in a pest-house. Deborah sobbed openly as the bell on the First Church on the Upper Green tolled out the death of its beloved pastor.

"Why didn't he get the innoculation?" cried Deborah.

"He never found the time," said the old sexton sadly. "He was too busy helping people."

"He was the best man I ever knew," said Deborah, her tears flowing. "He was religious, but he was with the world too. It seems he cared for the bodies of people as well as their souls."

"Aye," said the old sexton, "that's a true saying. He liked this world as well as the next and saw no harm in happiness."

Where would she go after she left the Thomases? Deborah sat in her old Sunday hide-out and turned the question over in her mind the next day. In one more year, her ten years of service would be over. What could a girl do in this world? She rubbed her hands together inside their mittens. It was too cold to stay long in her rock eyrie.

A year from now she would be eighteen and on her

own. She had counted on seeking the advice of Mr. Conant as she had always done, but now there was no one. It had been a long time since she had seen her mother. Perhaps Mistress could spare her for a week.

"Mistress, may I go to visit my mother?" asked Deborah after supper.

"Of course you may," said Mistress Thomas, "and you shall ride the stage. A handsome girl like you should not be walking the public roads in such cold weather, and it is not fitting for you to beg rides on farmers' carts. I will pay the fare myself. You are a good girl, Deborah. I don't know what I shall do when you leave us next year."

Deborah savored every minute of her first stage ride. Oh, if only the driver would make a wrong turn and take her to Boston instead, but she arrived in Plymouth without adventures.

Mother was very gray now, her shoulders bent, her hands stiff with blue veins standing out like cords. Hannah was married and living in Plymouth with her young husband and new baby. Nehemiah and Sylvia did most of the work now, tending to Mother and Uncle Nehemiah. Jonny, Ephraim, and Elisha were all fighting in the war, getting out to work for a few months at a time and then going back to fight.

"They say down in Middleborough that General Washington wants men he can count on, soldiers who enlist for a long time," said Deborah, settling back in her chair while Sylvia brought her a cup of hot cider.

"How could they?" asked Mother. "The soldiers have to go home to plant the crops and harvest and see their families."

"I don't know how they will do it," said Deborah. "Maybe they will have to pay the soldiers regularly. I see why they must be regularly enlisted, the way the British soldiers are, or we'll lose the war despite the good news of the defeat of General Burgoyne by short-term militia."

"How knowledgeable you are, Deborah," said Mother. "By a year from now I hope you will have found a husband worthy of you."

"Heavens, Mother, I don't want to get married in a year," cried Deborah in alarm. "Nobody's asked me, and besides I don't want to get all bogged down like Hannah and Mistress Thomas. Not yet."

"And what will you do with yourself, pray?" asked Mother. "Of course you must get married. What else is there for you to do?"

"I can hire out as a spinner or a weaver," said Deborah desperately. "I'm as strong as a man. I can do farm work."

"Don't be silly," said Mother. "Remember you're a Bradford."

"I'll find something. Just please don't go looking for a husband for me."

VI

1778–1781: In 1778 France came to the aid of the United States. In 1781 Cornwallis surrendered at Yorktown.

As Deborah's eighteenth birthday approached, she became more and more restless. Jacob was four now, Elizabeth seven, and Abraham nine. Mistress Thomas' hands were freed from baby care so that she could spend more time in the kitchen and dairy, and Deborah set up a dame school for the Thomas children.

Deacon Thomas came into the kitchen in October

with the news that the French were pouring into Boston.

"They eat frogs whole," said Abraham.

"I should wash your mouth with soap for such vulgarity," said his mother.

"That's what they used to say when the French were our enemy in the French and Indian Wars," said Deacon Thomas.

"I'm glad they're on our side now," said Deborah. "Oh, this is great news. Now we'll win the war for sure. I wish I could see a Frenchman. I'm part French, Abraham, and I don't eat frogs."

Abraham chewed his dried beef thoughtfully and looked at Deborah with new respect.

"I've been thinking of your future, Deborah," said the Deacon. "I believe I can help you get the job as schoolteacher for the Middleborough summer school if you'll stay with us through the winter."

"But, sir, how could I? Why, I've never even been to school. Besides, I have a bone felon from spinning. How can I teach writing when I must hold my finger out stiff?"

"No matter. You've had good experience teaching my children. There aren't many schoolmasters left, with all the Middleborough men going out on alarms to help the Rhode Islanders fight off the British fleet."

"Maybe the French will drive the British from Newport and the rest of Rhode Island," said Deborah.

Ransom and Deacon both took muskets and went out on a Rhode Island alarm that winter. Mistress objected vigorously, but Deborah helped clean the guns and mold the lead balls, seething with envy as Ransom swaggered and strutted and packed his knapsack.

"We'll make Massachusetts and Rhode Island safe from the British," he said.

"Nonsense," said Deborah. "They've been harassing the Rhode Island ports for years. What makes you think you're going to do aught but catch cold?"

The Middleborough company marched away, only to return ten days later with no important victory to report. But Jacob thought his father and brothers were great heroes, and said so until Deborah was tempted to box his ears.

War and soldiers, that was all any of them from Deborah to Jacob could remember.

In June, Deborah began her schoolteaching. With tears and hugs, she packed her meager belongings and moved out of the loft room that had been her home for over ten years to the home of Mr. Abner Bourne, who lived next door to the school in the center of the village.

Deborah faced her twenty pupils from behind the scarred teacher's desk where a Bible, a few Psalters, a spelling book, some New England Primers, and her own copy of GULLIVER'S TRAVELS lay. Deborah took the long teacher's stick and put it away. It made no sense to beat a child into learning.

A-b, *ab*, *i-b*, *ib*, went the lessons. The pupils paid her in Continental money, vegetables, fruit, and a few yards of cloth. The food she took to the Bournes for board, and the cloth was used for her clothes. As for the money, it was so worthless that it did not go far, and prices were outrageous whenever there was anything to buy in the scantily supplied shops.

For two summers she taught, and in the winters she hired out as a weaver and spinner, going from house to house for a few weeks at a time.

I'm never at a loss for work to do, she thought, but oh it's dull. All the men are gone, nobody has parties any more, all the excitement in this world is reserved for men. But she kept such thoughts to herself. They would never do in the female gossip around the loom.

How she missed Mr. Conant. Since his death, she had gone reluctantly to the Congregational Church. One Sunday morning in autumn she awoke, listened to the early church bell, and then turned over and considered going back to sleep. Mistress Bourne was in the kitchen below. Deborah wondered what would happen if she suddenly refused to go to church. She grinned, thinking of the excitement it would cause. Mistress Bourne would scream and threaten to invoke the Colonial Sunday law of church attendance.

And I can tell her that we are no longer a colony, that we believe ourselves to live in the United States now, and that there is therefore no longer a colonial law of churchgoing, she thought. But word would get around that Deborah Sampson had gone too far in her outlandish ideas and her work orders would dwindle, and then she would have to go home to Mother and marry that jackass over in Plymouth.

"Deborah, get up and come along to meeting," called Mistress Bourne.

An intriguing compromise struck Deborah. When she entered the kitchen dressed for church Deborah said casually to Mistress Bourne, "I have decided not to attend church with you this morning."

"What?" Mistress Bourne turned indignantly to Deborah.

"I am going to the Baptists instead to hear a revival sermon. I hear that the Reverend Mr. Asa Hunt is a mighty preacher, and that people are joining in great numbers," said Deborah, relishing Mistress Bourne's astonishment.

Mistress Bourne sniffed. "You're a headstrong one, Deborah," she said. "You're of age to do as you please, but the church of my ancestors is good enough for me."

"Perhaps it is not good enough for me, though," said Deborah so piously that Mistress Bourne could not take offense, yet she glared suspiciously at her.

Deborah walked to the Rock Church on the edge of town. She glanced down at the new kid gloves she had bought with her weaving money. She wished she had not had to spend so much for this elegance, but she enjoyed the stir her entrance caused.

Mr. Hunt preached long and loudly, exhorting his congregation to be saved. The next day, Mr. Abraham Camp, the new Congregational minister, paid a call on Deborah.

"It grieves me that you were not with us yesterday," he said.

The way gossip traveled in Middleborough he must certainly have heard a dozen times that Deborah Sampson had gone over to the Baptists, Deborah decided.

"I thought it would be interesting to see what makes people sometimes go to different churches nowadays," said Deborah.

"The Baptists might go to Hell," said Mr. Camp darkly.

"The Congregationalists likewise," said Deborah stoutly. "I'm not sure what I believe about Hell, but now that I'm older I don't subscribe to all of the Catechism of the Assembly of Divines."

"What! You are renouncing the religion of your Puritan ancestors?" cried Mr. Camp, shocked indeed.

"Some of it," said Deborah calmly. "I don't believe for one moment that a merciful God, which Mr. Conant said we have, would damn infants because they had not been baptized."

"What do the Baptists think on that?" asked Mr. Camp.

"That I don't know," said Deborah, "but whatever the beliefs are, I don't think the town should be forced to pay taxes to support any church. A man or a woman should decide where and if and when he will worship and pay the minister of his own free will. Many people are saying that."

On November 12, 1780, when Mr. Hunt exhorted

the people in his best revival fashion, Deborah stood up and became a Baptist.

But the change in churches did little to change the lack of purpose in her restless life. What am I good for, she asked herself. I can think better than Ransom or a half a dozen oafs I know, but because of these *skirts*—she jerked at her full linsey-woolsey skirt—I am hobbled for life.

Deborah read the papers avidly and followed each detail of the war. On October 19, 1781, Cornwallis surrendered at Yorktown. Deborah asked so many questions and listened so intently to the war talk that she almost felt she had been there herself. She had followed the Southern campaigns until she could draw marching maps for interested little boys. When the Tory uprisings, which had become very serious in some parts of the country, were put down, a peace would eventually be signed and the soldiers would come home to a bright new world.

What kind of world will it be for me, thought Deborah as she prepared for another winter of weaving. Her two summers of teaching had convinced her that she had not enough schooling of her own to continue. Besides, there had been complaints from some of the parents that she taught the girls improperly, that she neglected their needlework and knitting instruction to teach them about stars and faraway places, and that she had brushed off learning the Catechism as unimportant.

Whenever she saw Mother she was reminded of her duty to marry.

"Deborah, that merchant's son at Plymouth is

dying for a kind word from you. His father thinks you would make a fine, strong, wife."

"Then his father should buy him a slave. He'll get no kind word from me. He smells. I can't stand the rum he drinks and the fumes that surround him. I'll make my way as a weaver until something better comes my way."

"But Deborah, aren't you ever going to marry?" asked Hannah, proudly displaying her two round-faced children. "Whatever else will you do? You love children and have such a way with them."

Deborah pulled her nephew over onto her lap. "Of course I love children, and I'll marry when I have a mind to, but I haven't got a mind to right now. I want to learn a few more things about the world and the people in it. I want to find out who I am, myself, and what I can do."

"Silly talk," said Mother. "You're Deborah Sampson, and you have in your veins the best blood in the Colonies."

"In the United States," corrected Deborah.

"In the United States," conceded Mother. "You can sew and weave and spin and write and read and teach school, and you can tend sheep and run a dairy and even make a milking stool. Mistress Thomas says you are as handy with tools as a boy. And you can shoot a musket and skin a deer, she tells me. What can you do, indeed! I shall never understand you, Deborah. 'Tis because I let you go out in service too young."

"What else could you have done, Mother? There

was no other course open for a penniless widow with seven children. Perhaps when the war is over and we become the great nation that Mr. Jefferson predicts, then we women will have a better place in the world."

" 'Tis not likely," said Mother. " 'Tis against nature."

"But there may be many changes," persisted Deborah. "Jenny, my friend whose mother is a slave, said she thinks all the slaves will be freed some day. The town of Worcester did raise such a resolution."

"What wild talk. Anyhow, despite the surrender at Yorktown, there's still a good deal of fighting going on."

"That I know," said Deborah. "The muster men are beating the drums harder than ever and offering more bounty money than ever before. The enlistments are for three years now, and the men who go in are real soldiers. Continental soldiers they are called, the way General Washington wanted them from the start. There are harsh penalties for deserters nowadays."

"Deborah, I do believe you have the brains of your great-great-grandfather Bradford, who was said to be the brightest man in the Mayflower Company. But don't give yourself brain fever. 'Tis so dangerous for a girl to think too deep. It makes them die young."

"Pshaw, I've been hearing about brain fever all my life," said Deborah. "I'm not going to get brain fever or die young either, unless it's dying from seeing nothing more than Plymouth and Middleborough all my life."

She stalked out the door to see to the farm horse

that she had borrowed for her ride to Plymouth. There was nobody to pay her stage fare now.

"I always said that the way she used to ask *why* all the time was going to lead her into trouble," said Hannah, shaking her head. "If my children ever do that, I shall put a stop to it at once."

On the seventeenth of December, 1781, Deborah reached her twenty-first birthday. She awoke in the small bedroom she shared with Jenny at the Leonard's house, where she was weaving. Jenny had already left her half of the bed and was in the kitchen below banging the breakfast pots.

Deborah lay considering the day. Who knew or cared that this should be a great day in her life. With the strength of her old habit, she jumped out of bed and ran to the window to see what new marvel lay outside the walls of the room to make her forget her petty hurt. Down the snow-speckled road lay the tavern with a garish new sign posted on the door.

FORTUNE TELLER . . . NECROMANCER . . .

I READ THE FUTURE

WHAT DO THE STARS FORETELL FOR YOU?

What do the stars foretell? Deborah got into her clothes and stopped in the weaving room, where she lit the fire to warm it for her day's work. Now that young Sam had gone to war, his mother had turned his chamber into a loom room. Deborah was sorry he had gone, for she liked Sam with his zany ways and his friendly smile. She had stood and waved to him as he marched away several months ago.

Nowadays, mused Deborah, as she blew the fire, the soldiers had uniforms issued to them, not like the early days of the war when each man furnished his own. Yes, Middleborough had finally voted to outfit the town men who went to war. The town had been required to furnish fifty thousand pounds of meat for the Army. How some people had grumbled at the idea of a central government telling them what to do.

Sam's clothes were in the chest where Deborah was perched as she watched the fire blaze. Suddenly an idea so wonderful and so simple came to her that it was as though a great birthday gift had been laid in her lap by generous gods.

"Jenny," she called, rushing down the stairs, her eyes sparkling and her voice gay. "Jenny, Jenny, this is a great day." She grabbed Jenny and twirled her around in a breathless dance.

"Deborah, you stop that foolishness," admonished Jenny, straightening her apron. "What's got into you this time of the morning?"

"Good spirits," said Deborah, scooping a hot johnnycake into her mouth. "I'm twenty-one years old today and I'm going to the fortuneteller. Don't tell anybody."

"You wouldn't dare!" exclaimed the scandalized Jenny. "Why Deborah, ladies don't do that. They'd run you out of town."

Deborah leaned over and whispered in Jenny's ear. "I'm going in disguise. Nobody will know who I am."

"Oh goosy, how could you disguise yourself?"

"I'm going to put on Sam Leonard's suit that's upstairs in the chest. I'm going to pretend I'm a traveler and go to the tavern. Oh, what a lark!"

"Deborah, you put on men's clothes! You'll go to HELL if you do that. Don't, don't," implored the horrified Jenny.

"Well, I'm going to do it," said Deborah, grinning at the thought of it. "I'll take my chances on going to Hell. Shh, here comes Mistress Leonard."

After breakfast, Deborah locked herself in the weaving room and took Sam's clothes from the chest. She slipped the waistcoat over her dress. Perfect. The breeches she held up in front of herself. She rummaged in the chest. There were shirts, boots, hose, and hat. It was a good omen that nothing was missing for the escapade.

"Deborah, Deborah," called Mistress Leonard, pounding on the door.

Deborah pushed the clothes back into the chest and opened the door. "The latch must have accidentally fallen," she said, slightly flustered. "Mistress Leonard, look, how do you like the puce color of the wool?"

"Splendid," said Mistress Leonard approvingly. That Deborah was a wizard with the weaving.

All day, Deborah sang at her work. Why had such a thought never come to her before? That night, when the house was quiet, Deborah piled Sam's clothes into her apron and took them to her bedchamber. With scared giggles, Jenny helped Deborah dress. When the last button was fastened, Jenny looked at her critically.

"Perfect, except"—here Jenny buried her head in her feather pillow to keep from laughing aloud—"your bosom gives you away."

Deborah surveyed her bustline in the shadowy mirror.

"Stop laughing, Jenny." She shook the girl. "You'll ruin everything if you make too much noise. Here, take this linen cloth and bind it around me tight. See? Now pin me in."

Jenny got her giggles under control and strapped Deborah into the tight band. Deborah took a deep breath, found she could breathe, and put on her shirt and coat again.

"Deborah, how are you going to get through the kitchen? You know that if you go down those creaking stairs and open the door bolt below, that Mistress will be on you before you can hush her screams. Deborah, you're *insane!*"

"I'll get out, never fear," said Deborah, strutting about getting used to pants. She opened the window and reached her hand out for the maple limb that brushed the side of the house.

"Good-by, Jenny. Open the window when you hear a knock."

Deborah slid down the tree and landed in the snow. Luck was with her, for the tavern lights were still burning. She pranced a little, trying out the feeling of power that the clothes gave her. She was no longer Deborah Sampson, but an independent, twenty-one-year-old person. She shook the coins she had remembered to put in her pocket and swaggered into the tavern.

The fortuneteller was drinking stout by the fire.

"Serve you, sir?" asked the barman.

"Naught for me," said Deborah, making her voice as deep as possible. "I have come to consult the fortuneteller."

The fortuneteller put down his mug and disappeared into the curtained corner of the taproom.

"Sir," he called in a moment.

Deborah stepped quickly into his booth. In another minute the barkeep would surely have asked whence she came, and her planned answer of "merely traveling" would have sounded weak indeed late on a December night.

The fortuneteller studied Deborah's face and palm, touched her temple, and asked for money.

"You are a very young man," he said, "but you would like to appear older. I see a great future in your hand. Whatever enterprise you undertake will succeed. You are planning an adventure now. Do it. It will succeed. You will go in the Army and be a good soldier. You will marry well, but not for a few years yet."

Deborah slipped out of the tavern so quickly that she gave nobody a chance to speak to her.

"Who was that fellow?" asked the kitchen maid, who had come in to collect the dirty glasses.

"Who knows?" said the fortuneteller, picking up his

mug again. "Some runaway apprentice, no doubt. I told him he would succeed at what he undertook. And so he will. The young usually do if they've a will."

Deborah ran down the moonlit road, leaping in the air to click her heels together for sheer joy. Then she remembered that someone might be looking out the window and come out to investigate such unseemly high spirits. She could hardly tell them that she had reached a tumultuous decision. *She would make herself her own suit of clothes to use at will.*

In her clothes box she had a piece of homespun that she had made during an idle time last year. She had planned to sell it when she could get a good price. How lucky that she had not. She would cut it and make it into a man's suit and wear it to use—oh, the possibilities were endless.

She climbed the tree and rapped on the window. Jenny let her into the room, her finger on her lips. "Mistress is stirring," she whispered.

"Jenny, Deborah," Mistress Leonard rapped on the door. Deborah dived under the covers, boots and all. "Is aught amiss?"

"No, Mistress Leonard," said Deborah. "We were only fastening a loose shutter."

"It's all fastened now," added Jenny, trying to keep her voice steady.

Deborah quaked as Mistress Leonard scuffed down the hall in her carpet slippers, and then she burst into such a shaking fit of laughter that Jenny stuffed the

116

feather pillow in her mouth. When Deborah could finally control herself, Jenny took the pillow off and shook her.

"Don't you ever do such a thing again, Deborah Sampson," sputtered the enraged Jenny. "You'll get yourself and me too in such trouble as never happened before."

"Jenny," said Deborah, peeling off Sam's suit and grinning wickedly in the dark, "I've only just begun. I'm going to make my own suit and go—oh, maybe I'll go to Philadelphia."

"You'll do no such thing," said Jenny, aghast. "A prank's a prank, but that would be a mortal sin. I won't promise to cover up for you." Poor Jenny was on the point of tears.

"Wait and see," teased Deborah. She had not felt so lighthearted in years.

The next morning, Deborah was up an hour ahead of time, singing at the loom. When Mistress Leonard departed for a quilting party, Deborah pulled her material from her box, locked the door, and began cutting her suit, using Sam's for a model. She had helped Mistress Thomas make suits many times.

In a few days, with her last bit of cash, she had a pair of men's boots made at the cobbler's. "For my sister's husband," she explained. "His foot is the same size as mine."

And now it all lay in readiness, her man's outfit, her escape hatch to a life of adventure and prosperity. Suppose she put the clothes on this minute and ran away to

Philadelphia. What would she use for money? Mistress Leonard would pay her for her weaving work soon, but that would not support her for more than a week of travel. Yet the fortuneteller had told her that whatever she undertook would succeed.

What else had the fortuneteller said? He had said that she would join the Army. It was easy enough for the fortuneteller to predict that of any young man nowadays, but maybe he was pointing the way. Crazy notions chased around and around in her head.

The muster man was beating the drum at Mr. Israel Wood's house now, offering more bounty money than ever before. If she had fooled the fortuneteller into believing that she was a man, why couldn't she fool the muster man and soldiers in the Army? Back and forth she walked with her work as she tried to make up her mind.

She was finishing off the last of the piece on the loom when Jenny brought her a letter from Mother. Jenny watched as Deborah read the letter, bit her lips, and thrust it in her pocket in annoyance.

"Is something wrong?" asked Jenny anxiously.

"Nothing that anybody can help," said Deborah grimly.

When Jenny left the room, Deborah read the letter again. The merchant's son had made a formal proposal of marriage through her mother. Mother wanted her to come home, learn to know the man, and agree to the marriage. It would be a wise one, said Mother, for the man was rich and eager.

Deborah tore the letter into bits, brushed her hands together, and felt the luxury of a firm decision steal warmly over her. Tonight she would put on her suit, go to Israel Wood's house, and enlist.

That night, while Jenny stood by wringing her hands and pleading with her, Deborah resolutely put on her new clothes. "Jenny," she said, turning around for inspection, "I am now Timothy Thayer. I am going out for the evening." She tried to laugh as she rubbed her hands together to hide her nervousness.

Mr. Thayer, she said to herself as she walked down the road after sliding down the maple tree. I'll say I'm from Carver. She hurried along to the sound of the muster man. Could she get away with it? Her supper rose alarmingly to her throat. If I turn around now and go back to the Leonard's, I can sell this suit of clothes and go home to Mother and get married, she thought.

"I won't," she said aloud. "I'm going to see the world and serve my country, and this is the way."

She opened the door and stepped into the room. It was late, but the man was there, hopefully watching the door.

"Come to join up?" he invited.

"Yes, sir," said Deborah, keeping her voice as deep and steady as she could.

"Then sign here," said the recruiter. "Write where you can be found when the time comes for the new company to muster, a matter of a week or two. That done, here is your money."

Deborah picked up the quill the man handed her, noting his sigh of relief. It was hard to get recruits for the Army now, even with the reward of enlistment money. People were tired of war, and the Continental money wasn't worth much. To hook a healthy young man nowadays was an achievement for a poor recruiter. He took what came and no questions asked.

"Very good, Mr. Thayer," said the man as Deborah signed her new name.

"Mr. Who?" came a cracked old voice from the settle by the fire. "Mr. Whoever-he-is holds his finger the way Deb Sampson do."

Deborah nearly dropped her pen, but she tried to keep her stiff finger steady as she wrote "Timothy Thayer, Carver, Mass." She recognized the voice as that of Mr. Wood's old mother, the worst gossip in town, and very keen of sight despite her years.

"I am not acquainted with that lady," said the muster man, "but I don't believe this fellow's finger will keep him from shooting a musket."

"No, sir," said Deborah-Timothy in her deepest voice. "I got this bone felon from shooting too much."

"We will send for you very soon, Mr. Thayer," said the recruiter, ignoring the old woman. "Good night."

Whew! Deborah stepped out into the night and fingered the crisp money in her pocket. Why not give Mr. Thayer another chance. There was a new tavern about two miles from town where her face would not be known. The weather was good, and she might as well enjoy her evening out.

She strode into the tavern feeling puffed up with power after her long walk.

"What'll it be, sir?" asked the host.

"Stout," said Deborah, pulling one of the new bills from her pocket with a flourish. It was good to be a man.

When the weaving job was finished at the Leonards the next week, Deborah went out to visit the Thomases. She was always welcome there, and she had to lie low until she heard that the new company was ready to form, at which time she would get into her disguise and march away with the Army. Too, she had to have some excuse for not going to Plymouth, where her mother was waiting for an answer. Visiting the Thomases was a good reason.

Deborah felt guilty thinking of Mother's despair and her friends' sorrow when she disappeared into the Army. They would think she was dead probably. And then when the war was over, she would come home and tell everything, unless of course she was discovered and sent home in disgrace. Or killed, she considered soberly.

The day after she arrived at the Thomas house, Deborah and Elizabeth, now a pretty ten-year-old, walked to Sproat's Tavern to deliver the eggs, as Deborah had done so often in years past. It was a bonny afternoon. Elizabeth played outside by the measuring post while Deborah stepped into the kitchen to hand the eggs to the cook. Through the open door into the taproom she could hear a voice that she recognized as the muster man.

"Do you know anyone in these parts named Timothy Thayer?" he was asking.

Deborah froze.

"Thayer?" someone answered. "Not in this town I don't. There's Thayers up at Kingston."

"This is Timothy Thayer. Came in and enlisted from Carver and took the muster money. But there's no Timothy Thayer there. If I don't find the man, I'll be held responsible for the money. There's an old lady who says I was duped, that Timothy Thayer was a local girl dressed up like a man to steal the muster money. I can scarce credit that, but then I can't find Thayer, so—"

Deborah stepped out of the kitchen. The cook, busy counting the eggs, had not heard, but word would get around. She must act quickly.

"Elizabeth," she called, "please run to Mistress Leonard's and see if Jenny is within. Ask her to meet me in the willow grove beside the cemetery."

How stupid she had been to enlist in her own town. She should have chosen some other place where she was not known.

She went to the cemetery and waited impatiently until she saw Jenny come out of the Leonard kitchen. "Run to the brook, Elizabeth," she called, "and see if the first violets are out."

She turned to Jenny. "You may never see me again. I want you to do something for me."

"Deborah, what do you mean? I told you no good would come of your putting on those men's clothes!"

"Don't try to understand me, Jenny. Just please do as I say," said Deborah desperately. "Any minute now, people may be saying that I enlisted under a false name and stole the muster money."

"En*listed!*" cried Jenny so loudly that Deborah placed her finger over her mouth.

"Yes, enlisted under the name Timothy Thayer, in the Army. But I didn't intend to steal the muster money. I meant to go through with it and be there when the new company was formed, but now they suspect that Timothy Thayer was me—well I can't tell you any more. All I want you to do is give the muster money back when they come around looking for me, because I don't want the man to suffer the loss. I'll be gone by then, maybe for good."

Jenny's eyes began to spill over with tears. "Deborah, you've got no sense. For all they say you have more brains than are good for you, I think you're just plain dumb and stupid. What are you planning to do?"

"Jenny, I can't tell you. Just give them the money and get my name off the list. You don't have to let on you know more than that. But if you have a chance to see my mother and Mistress Thomas, tell them I have always loved them and will, no matter what happens. And here, Jenny, I want you to have these gloves." Deborah took her treasured gloves from her pocket and handed them to Jenny. "I guess you are the only girl friend I have."

Jenny was crying openly.

"Stop crying, Jenny, if you are my friend. Be sure to return that money so Deborah Sampson will leave a good name behind when people think she is dead. Come on, Elizabeth," she called. "I'll race you to the bridge."

Lifting her long skirt, she ran down the road beside Elizabeth like a fleet-footed schoolgirl.

VII

1782: "Another call which proved to be the last one necessary to supply the Massachusetts line of its Continental Army was made by a resolve passed March 8, 1782, wherein it was directed that 1500 men were to be raised to serve three years or the War, under the usual provisions applying to Continental enlistments. If the town did not raise its quota a substitute could be hired."

From the Introduction to

MASSACHUSETTS SOLDIERS AND SAILORS OF
THE REVOLUTIONARY WAR

Among the recruits was, unknown to the authorities, a woman.

It was four in the afternoon when Elizabeth and Deborah returned to the Thomas farm. Deborah helped Mistress Thomas prepare supper. The sooner the evening meal was over the sooner the family would go to bed and the sooner she could put on her suit and escape, stealing out into the night like a thief, if only the town authorities did not come looking for her before nightfall.

The Thomas family was at the table when they

heard horse hoofs galloping into the dooryard. Jacob jumped from the table and ran to the door. This was it. Deborah grabbed the edge of the table until her knuckles turned white.

"Your cows have broken the fence in your lower pasture," shouted Mr. Bennet.

"I'll run them home," cried Deborah, jumping up so energetically that she nearly upset the table.

"Let Silas do it," said Mistress Thomas, looking at Deborah in surprise. "You no longer have to do the chores here."

"Oh, please, I truly would like to," insisted Deborah nervously.

"You're a strange one, Deborah. You look quite pale. Maybe a run on the meadow would put some color in your cheeks," said Mistress Thomas.

"She's pale for love," said Jacob. "I heard Ransom say so."

"Mind your own business," said his mother sharply. "But Deborah, we heard of your marriage offer. I hope you'll take it."

"I must get the cows," said Deborah, running out the door.

The last candle was out and the kitchen fire was banked. The childish breathing of Jacob and Elizabeth, who were sleeping in the loft room with her, and the Deacon's snores were the only sounds in the house. Stealthily she reached in her satchel for her precious disguise and put it on. With boots in hand she crept down the familiar steep stairs to the kitchen. Someone turned over in bed. Deborah froze. For once she had no ready explanation on her tongue.

She stood there until the quiet came back and then lifted the latch and let herself out into the spring night. Her friends might think she had taken her own life, she thought sadly. They would search the farm and the surrounding country. She walked fast, knowing she must get out of the area. With luck she could reach Taunton by morning where she might fall in with some stranger headed for an enlistment headquarters. I will call myself Robert Shirtliff, she decided.

But first she must cut off some of her hair. She sat down on a stone wall and, pulling out the pocket knife she had bought last year with some of her weaving money, she hacked her hair to shoulder length, tucked the rest into her cap as the other soldiers did, buried the hank of hair, and hurried on.

Another sunny day broke on the horizon as she entered Taunton Green. She paused a minute watching the gold rays, and, turning, looked straight into the eyes of William Bennet, Ransom's friend on the neighboring farm. Deborah ducked in panic into a back alley.

Had he recognized her? Would he go home and tell the Thomases? She looked over her shoulder. At least he wasn't following her. A baker woman was just opening her shop. Deborah darted into the open door and bought some stale bread. She took the bread in her hand and looked up and down the empty street. The woman looked at her suspiciously, and Deborah headed for the nearest woods.

She sat in the safety of the woods and ate the bread, finally falling asleep under the March sun. She awoke with a clearer head. What to do? Perhaps she should stay where she was in this protected spot for the rest of the day. At dark she could steal back to the Thomas farm and hide in her old eyrie. Maybe somehow she could find out if William had recognized her. I'm an outlaw now, she thought, and I must think outlaw thoughts.

She crept into her old Sunday hide-out and went sound asleep on her bed of ferns. After dark she fearfully stole across the back yard of the Thomas house and listened, quaking inside, by the shuttered window. The Thomases were awake; a crack of light showed around the edge of the sleeping-room window. She could hear Mistress sobbing quietly. Deborah felt sick with shame, but there was nothing to be done about it now.

"There, there, Susannah," she heard the Deacon say. "Perhaps she is not dead. Maybe she ran away to her relatives in Maine. She spoke of them a time or two. She didn't want to marry that man her mother picked for her. Girls have done that kind of thing before."

"But her clothes are here. What did she wear? Do you suppose there is a word of truth to the rumors in town that she tried to enlist in men's clothes?"

"Maybe she had other clothes we didn't know about," said the Deacon. "Whatever, I bank on seeing her again some day."

"I don't believe she's dead," said Jeremiah. "It's a trick. Deborah had too much fun to want to die."

"Dead or alive, she's not on this farm, I'll vouch," said Ransom. "We fellows searched everywhere, even her old hide-out that she thought I didn't know about."

Deborah felt the load lift from her mind. At least William had not recognized her, and she would be safe in the eyrie until tomorrow night. When the house was quiet, she would risk lifting the pantry window and filching some food. She was starving.

Lying in her eyrie, she made a decision. Why not go to sea like her Cousin Simeon Sampson, now a famous captain in the American Navy?

When he was a boy, he had escaped from pirates by dressing up like a girl. Now she was escaping by dressing like a boy. She would sign on a privateer as a cabin lad. Nobody would ever find her there. Tomorrow night she would head for New Bedford.

Her eyes popping with the wonders of the world beyond Middleborough, Deborah strode into the busy town of New Bedford two days later. Down the hill lay the harbor full of ships, the docks astir with a motley lot of sunburned sailors whose speech fell strangely on Deborah's ears. Up and down the streets she went, gawking at everything.

When she ordered a platterful of fried clams and a cup of biting hot coffee for supper at a tavern, a swarthy sailor with half his teeth missing flopped down beside her.

"Looking for work?" he asked. "There's a berth for a waiter on a privateer sailing tomorrow. It has an American commander, if you have a leaning to patriotism."

"I'm looking for a berth," said Deborah eagerly.

"Runaway?" asked the man.

"Of course not," said Deborah. "I'm a free man. Robert Shirtliff is my name." It was the first time she had spoken it, but it fell easily from her tongue.

The man banged his glass for more grog. "You've got no beard, Bobby. You're not old enough to be a free man."

"That's my affair," said Deborah crustily.

"Don't get mad. You're just the lad we need for our ship. My name is Hines. I'll pay for your vittles if you'll come with me."

Deborah looked up to meet the eyes of the serving girl who hovered behind Hines, frowning deeply at him. Then she raised her eyebrows at Deborah. But Deborah ignored her. What marvelous good fortune to have a meal paid for and a job as fast as all that.

She followed Hines over the tarry ropes on the ship's deck and down the steep, evil-smelling hatch to the Captain's cabin. The Captain lifted his small eyes from his papers and looked over his fat belly at Deborah, who was suddenly filled with terrified misgivings.

"Can you shave me? Hold a pot for the queasy? Empty the slops? Fix my vittles?" he asked, giving a semblance of an ingratiating smile.

Deborah stared at the man, speechless. Her stomach lurched at the thought of touching him. She must have been insane to have thought for one instant of going to sea.

"What do they call you? Bobby? You're hired." said the Captain.

What did he mean, she was hired? She had agreed to nothing.

"You look full young, Bobby," said the Captain overlooking her silence, "but we'll fix that. We'll age you before you get back to your mother. I guarantee that. I'll give you an advance of money to seal the bargain."

"Just hold the money for me," said Deborah cautiously. "I have some cash upon me." She had to get out of there and run as fast as she could as far away as possible from this foul-smelling ship. But it wasn't that easy.

"Show Bobby around, Hines," ordered the Captain.

Hines threw his arm around Deborah and led her through the filthy labyrinth of the ship and pointed out the twelve-inch shelf where the cabin boy slept. Deborah pulled away from him, but Hines seemed determined to keep his arm on Deborah's shoulder. "You'll have to help the ship's surgeon too," added Hines.

"I must go get my belongings I left at the tavern," said Deborah, backing away from Hines.

"See you get aboard before midnight," said Hines. "If you'd taken the money, the Captain wouldn't have let you ashore, gear or no gear."

"Don't worry about me," said Deborah. She left the ship and walked leisurely to the corner, and then, looking back to be sure that nobody was following her, she turned up the dark hill and ran for her life. She ducked into the tavern where she had been before to see the waitress. Perhaps those glances had meant an important message.

"I hope you didn't sign on," said the girl in a low voice. "It's your business, but you look gentle and could be taken in easy. The reason the cabin-boy berth is open is that the Captain is the meanest man on the seven seas. It's a scandal the way he treats his cabin boys. The last one died at sea, and nobody knows why."

Deborah shuddered. "I thank you, miss. I took no money from the man, and I'm leaving this town as fast as my feet will fly. He thinks I'm coming back tonight, though I agreed to nothing."

"Then hurry," said the girl. "You look to be a gentleman and should not have dealings with that man. Whether you agreed or not he is not above kidnaping you for the journey if he's taken a fancy to you. If you'd accepted the money, you'd be in terrible trouble."

Deborah raced out of town by back alleys and narrow lanes, heading for another night in the open. She had not slept under a roof since she put on men's clothes almost a week ago.

Luckily the weather was good. She burrowed down in a leftover haystack, pulled some of the prickly hay over herself, and looked at the stars. The North Star shone brightly above her, beckoning her north to Boston town.

The North Star was still shining four hours later when she woke up stiff with cold. She stood up and stretched, brushing the hay from her clothes. A few more nights like this and she would look like a vagabond indeed.

She felt in her pocket for her money. She must ration it carefully to survive in Boston until she could enlist. Enlisting seemed the most natural step in the world now. Not once had anyone challenged her manhood. Still, she had to be careful and wait a few weeks before she tried again in case the news had got about that a girl had fooled the muster man at Middleborough. She dug her hand in her pocket for her purse. The pocket was empty!

She turned her pockets inside out. Frantically she reached inside her waistcoat, but there was nothing there. She searched through the hay. Perhaps it had fallen from her pocket. At last she sat down and faced the bleak facts. That man Hines had picked her pocket when he had thrown his arm so persistently around her.

She bit her lips to fight back the girlish tears of anger and mortification that wanted to rise to her eyes in spite of her new mannish role. She thought of the long weary hours she had spent at the loom to earn that money.

It was dawn now, with the road beckoning under the new light. Perhaps in Boston dressed as a boy she could earn money much faster. A cow ambled in the pasture ahead, crunching on dewy fresh grass.

Deborah leaped the fence, caught the cow, and opening her mouth she gave herself a few squirts of milk straight from its udder. The cow held still, recognizing an experienced milker.

There's food to be had, she told herself cheerily, heading for the road before the farmer found her robbing his cow. She picked some tightly curled fern fronds and chewed them hungrily. They were better cooked with butter and water, but they filled the empty belly.

She chopped a pile of wood in exchange for dinner at a farmhouse. She slept in a barn and stole another drink from a friendly cow. A farmer's desperate widow paid her in Continental money to mend her broken plow and open her field for planting. Her son was overdue from the war, she said, and she could wait no longer to get her field started.

Deborah stayed there three days, working and eating, planning her trip to Boston. A new world was opening for her, she thought with relish. She could hardly wait.

When she arrived in Boston on the Middle Post Road, the great town lay before her. All that day she wandered about the town drinking in the sights. There was Faneuil Hall, and there was King's Chapel. She saw Sam Adams come out of the Customs House, and she saw the ships in the harbor.

That night she paid some of her precious money for a bed at an inn and a hot meal to go under her belt. The innkeeper was distracted, fussing and fuming because one of his grooms had helped himself to a ham and a pound of valuable coffee and disappeared. They were shorthanded for a boy at the stable that night.

"I'm handy with horses," said Deborah. "Try me."

"I'll give you a try," agreed the man. "You can start right now and save the price of a night's lodging by sleeping in the stable bunkroom with the other boys. I'm pressed for space with this town full of travelers."

Deborah bedded down with the boys, falling into the straw bunk with her clothes on like the rest of them. She knew how to take care of horses after her years on the farm. She went about her business, always a little aloof from the others, and, because her speech was more refined and her manner more gentle, the grooms left her alone except to tease her about her lack of beard. Nobody questioned her manhood.

For weeks every free moment she had she prowled the streets of Boston. Once, passing Mr. John Hancock's house on Beacon Street, she saw the gentleman himself. Another afternoon, while waiting for an answer to a message sent by her master, she peered into the window of Mr. Revere's silver shop and walked on to Griffin's Wharf, where they had dumped the tea that night in 1773. She stood there thinking back to the cold day at the Thomas farm, when she was only thirteen, and the news had come about the tea party. One of the other grooms from the inn sidled up to her.

"Hello," said Deborah in surprise.

"I saw you here, wasting Master's time," said the boy.

"I'm not wasting Master's time," said Deborah hotly. "I'm waiting for an answer to be written."

"What makes you think you're better than the rest of us?" asked the boy in a surly fashion.

"Me?" asked Deborah, surprised. "I don't think I'm better than anybody."

"Just watch your step," threatened the boy.

Deborah walked away. The answer must be ready for Master by now. What harm could he, a jealous fourteen-year-old boy do her? Plenty, she decided, if he incited the others to gang up on her and rough her up a bit. Perhaps they resented the fact that Master sent her on substantial errands and even had her read and write for him.

She had her week's wages in her pocket. She owed Master nothing, and all her clothes were on her back. Master could hire another boy with nothing lost. She would take the answer back to Master and disappear.

At dusk she headed out of town. She had decided to go across the Boston Neck to Roxbury and on to some town west of Boston and enlist. The time had come. Life in the Army would be easy now after living in such close quarters with the stableboys without detection. She hardly thought of herself as Deborah any more. The name Bobby Shirtliff rolled off her tongue with ease.

On May 20, 1782, in Bellingham, Massachusetts,

she jumped from the farmer's cart where she had begged a ride. The muster man was beating the drum in the town square.

"Thanks for the ride, but I've got a mind to enlist," said Deborah to the farmer. "I think I'm going soldiering."

"That's Eliphalet Thorpe beating that drum over there," said the farmer. "Go tell him I brought him a recruit."

"You look full young," said Captain Thorpe, "but we're scraping the bottom of the barrel now. A beard is no requirement. We'll put you down for the Uxbridge quota for three years, or the rest of the war. You'll be a man before you get out of the Army."

"Will I?" grinned Deborah, signing the name Robert Shirtliff with a flourish. "When and where do we muster?"

"Immediately, at Worcester. Here's your money. Get yourself there as soon as you can. This is a snappy company you're signed for. You'll get a uniform when you report."

"Who are the officers, sir?" asked Deborah, counting the pile of bills. The Uxbridge bounty was better than most.

"You'll be in the Fourth Massachusetts Regiment with General Paterson at the top, in Colonel Shepherd's Regiment, and in Captain Webb's Company."

Deborah fell in step with another recruit as they

walked along under the hot May sun. She took off her jacket and vest, letting the breeze cool her. Her companion stripped off his shirt as well.

"Let the sun shine on your bare back, Bobby. It's healthy."

"Not today," said Deborah hastily.

"You blush like a girl," said the man.

" 'Tis the sunburn on my face. Too much sun has a way of burning my skin. That's why I keep on my shirt."

Deborah passed unnoticed in the confusion of the new troops at Worcester, who were being issued fusees, knapsacks, and cartridge boxes. Her eyes lit up at the sight of the uniforms. The coat was blue lined with white, with white wings on the shoulders and cords on the arms and pockets. She was given a white waistcoat, breeches and stockings, half boots, and a cap with a cockade.

The men around her were peeling off their clothes to put on the new uniforms, but Deborah put hers over her arm and started away.

"Hey, where are you going?" asked the sergeant.

"To the tavern," said Deborah, thinking quickly. "My sister is there to take my suit home. I'll change and come back."

"Bring your sister back with you," shouted some-one.

Deborah went to the room in the hostel where she had spent the night before, and ordered hot water from the chambermaid. With the door locked she took off her

stinking, filthy suit. She had not been completely undressed since she had put on men's clothes in March.
She washed herself, luxuriating in the privacy, and put
on the new underdrawers she had bought as well as a
new linen bandage for her breast. When she was completely uniformed she called to the chambermaid.

"Take these clothes and clean them the best you
can. I'm going to sell them, cheap."

"Oh, sir, would you sell them to me? They would
fit my brother to a perfection. Then you need not be
troubled about the washing. Would you take this
for them?" The girl pulled a few bills from her pocket.

The clothes were worth more than this, thought
Deborah, but how hard a girl had to work to earn even
that much.

"Done," she agreed, "but I want no bill for the hot
water and I want this linen cloth washed and dried. I
will pick it up later."

The chambermaid looked curiously at the linen
binder. What would a man want with such a thing?
"You're very handsome," she said, examining Private
Robert Shirtliff in his new uniform. "I'll have the cloth
ready tonight."

"See that you do," said Deborah, turning away. She
would need that cloth for her own purposes, being a
woman.

The girl continued to stare at Deborah. "Enjoy
how clean you feel today. I've seen the soldiers come

through here thick with lice and smelling to Heaven. They never get a chance to change their clothes from one year to the next. That pretty uniform will be grimy in a week."

That will be all to the good for me, thought Deborah wryly. Then she remembered she was a soldier, a bona-fide, swashbuckling, soldier.

"Get along with you," she said to the maid. "I've got to clean my gun and learn the manual of arms this afternoon. I'm due on the parade ground in half an hour."

And she strutted out of the room as cocky as any other private.

For twelve days they marched to West Point. The weather drizzled and dripped, and an unseasonable cold swept the land after the gentle days of early spring. Deborah, for all her experience of sleeping under the stars, developed a red, running nose, and her coughing at night brought growls from the men who shared her sleeping quarters in barns and taverns.

One night the recruits, their uniforms as bedraggled as veterans', gathered around a fire at an inn. Deborah's feet ached. The issued boots were not nearly as comfortable as the ones she had sold to the chambermaid in Worcester. The hot fire made her head dizzy, and she slipped forward, close to fainting.

The innkeeper's wife was all concern. "Ah, he is

too young to be in the war. This lad is hardly ready to leave his mother."

"Bobby is stronger than you think," said the corporal. "He marches with the best of them and never complains."

"All the more reason to treat him well tonight then. He shall take my place in bed with my husband. He's too sick to sleep on the floor with the others tonight," said the kindly woman.

Deborah slept in her uniform as usual that night despite the host's offer of a nightshirt. "Soldiers are used to sleeping in their clothes. If they take off their breeches at night, they are too likely to wake up with none to put on," she said. She slept soundly beside the old man despite his snores.

By the time they reached West Point, Deborah felt she had been in the Army all her life. Bobby had fallen into place as a mild-mannered boy, a bit standoffish but ready enough to do his share or more. The older men looked out for him, thinking him the kind of lad they would like to have for their own son.

She was assigned to a rotten tent with eight other infantrymen. Nobody minded that she chose to sleep under the stars instead. At night she fell onto her tick of hay and slept from sheer exhaustion. Thank goodness, there was no fighting yet, as the infantry were set immediately to work alongside the engineers to complete the last details on the Colonnade, a beautiful new building where the officers sat to drink the health of General Washington.

It had been dedicated a few days before in honor of the alliance with France, with three cheers for the new-born Dauphin. Deborah welcomed the construction work. Her company was assigned to rebuilding the Upper Hudson fortifications and barracks. She had bound up the Thomas boys' cuts without a thought of queasiness, but her stomach felt uneasy whenever she remembered that eventually she would meet bloodshed on the battlefield.

Deborah was in line for her rations one morning in June when the corporal bellowed her name to join a scouting party to march south to fight Tories. Deborah said her prayers and took a deep breath. She would find out now if a girl had as much courage as a boy.

Laden with her gun and ammunition, her rations and canteen, she marched in her wretched boots to the no man's land between the British in New York City and the Americans in West Point, through Tory country all the way.

"Dutch Tories," said Ike, one of her tent mates, a graying bachelor who had adopted a protective uncle-like air toward Deborah. "They're mean, snipers, won't come out in the open and fight like soldiers. Don't stray off. You tend to get off alone too much, Bobby lad. 'Taint healthy."

"I'll remember that," said Deborah. Until I need to hide my female body in the bushes away from the rest of you, she thought, nursing her ever-present secret.

They crossed the Hudson at Stony Point after marching down the west side of the river and spending the night at Tarrytown. Because she was the youngest,

Deborah was bedded down in the hayloft of the tavern stable, glory be.

The next morning they were divided into groups, Deborah assigned to Ensign Town. They crept through the woods, staying off the road, glad for the dirty uniforms that camouflaged their bodies. They were ordered to go as far as possible into the enemy lines and return with news of the enemy position.

It seemed to Deborah that she crawled like a hungry worm for uncountable days until they reached Harlem, eight miles from the city of New York. By day they lay low, hidden in a swamp, and by night she and three others went all the way to the British camp when the sergeant ordered them back to White Plains, where they would pool their information with other groups.

So far they had escaped Delancey's Raiders. The men whispered about that vicious group as they crawled under the stars. Deborah was so tired she felt nothing. She had passed the point of soreness and hunger. She no longer even thought of the matter of courage. Automatically she did as she was told, trying to preserve life until she got back to West Point. Between Sing Sing and Tarrytown, when the danger seemed to be over, they were walking erect and in single file when a bullet whizzed over her head and lodged in a pine tree.

Delancey's Raiders had found them.

"Withstand two rounds and then fire," shouted Ensign Town.

Deborah stood on the line and coolly shot her gun. At that instant a bullet went through her hat, and she felt warm blood run down her face.

"Take cover, every man for himself!" shouted the Ensign. "We're outnumbered twenty to one."

Deborah ran through the underbrush, faint and dizzy, the blood running freely. Finally coming to a sink hole with a protective log over it, she fell into it, half conscious, and fainted.

It was dark when she came to. The blood had dried on the side of her head. She was sick at her stomach and dizzy, but at least she was alive. She sat up and listened to the stillness. They had overlooked her and gone away.

She tried to stand, and found she could. Oh, how her head ached. The Hudson River was near, she remembered. Unsteadily she found her way to it and stumbled along the river's edge to Tarrytown, where she found the remnants of her own group.

Thank God, their losses were light she discovered as she stretched out on the floor at an inn. They had won the battle after all. Colonel Sproat with his Massachusetts men had come to the rescue and routed the Delancey Raiders. What would Colonel Sproat think if he had seen her and recognized her as the girl who delivered eggs to his kitchen all those years? Deborah smiled thinking of it.

"I'm glad you can smile, Bobby," said Ike, who, with a bloodsoaked rag around his arm, had been preparing to go out looking for her despite the advice of his comrades who had given her up for dead.

"Your wound isn't much, just a scratch," said the

doctor as he washed the caked blood from her head. "You'll be fine in a day or so."

Someone gave her a cup of wine and a piece of bread to eat. She lay down on the bed she was to share with Ike and slept around the clock.

Back at West Point, Private Bobby Shirtliff was now a veteran. She sat around the campfire at night and added to the yarns the soldiers spun.

"I was at Yorktown too," she bragged, re-creating the battle from the newspaper accounts she had read, until she half believed it herself.

Food was always a problem. As the soldiers had little to keep them busy in the summer of 1782, the local Patriot farmers hired them and paid them in food for the soldiers' mess. Deborah volunteered for farm duty. Except that she was dressed in comfortable pants, she might have been spending her usual summer day at the Thomas farm.

Working in the fields she found the privacy she missed in the camp. She even found a hide-out, a cave near the riverbank, that reminded her of her old eyrie at Middleborough. She could steal away there when she needed to be alone.

As winter approached, half the duties of the men were to find fuel. Her company worked hard all day cutting and hauling wood and returned to the camp famished.

There was always grumbling about food, but one night it was worse than ever. "I'm fit to die with eating nothing but cow heels and tripe," snapped the corporal, rubbing his rumbling stomach.

The Captain agreed. The food didn't come because the contractors and the commissaries haggled and bickered while the soldiers starved. At least that was what the men said as they endlessly discussed their empty stomachs.

"The Captain is asking for volunteers for a foray on a Tory smokehouse that's loaded and waiting for the British Army," said the sergeant. "How about you, Bobby?"

Deborah ran to muster, straightening her ragged cap and giving her baggy breeches an expert hitch. The only good thing about this eternal hunger was that she kept so thin. Breeches might give away a fat female behind.

"Let me go, sir," said Deborah eagerly. "I'm small and I can run fast too." This was her dish of tea, pitting her wits against the other side in a daring game.

"That's right, sir," said the sergeant. "Bobby here can run fast as a deer, and he knows how to keep himself hid when he wants. He can do things an older man can't."

The Captain looked at the slight boy. "Very well, Shirtliff, we'll count on you to bring us some bacon. You'll have a fight. The Tories are guarding that barn with all the men they can raise in the neighborhood, but we think the guards mostly sit around the kitchen fire."

The party of twelve men, their muskets on the ready, crept through the woods.

"Here's the plan, Bobby," whispered the sergeant when they reached the rendezvous point at dusk. "Leave your gun here, and at midnight you crawl in the smokehouse through the low window on the east. The rest of us will surround the place, keeping on our bellies, and take care of the guards outside."

"Aye, sir," said Deborah. The times she had crept through the smokehouse window at Deacon Thomas' on dares from the boys would pay off tonight.

"Cut down the hams and push the meat out the window, but set fire to the place before you escape."

"Set fire?" asked Deborah dubiously.

"Aye. In the confusion they might not even know we're stealing meat. We'll be out there pulling meat away as fast as you pass it out. Then we beat it to the rendezvous, loaded with meat. Ohhhh." The sergeant wiped the saliva from his lips with the back of his hand.

Deborah lay on her empty stomach until the October night was dark and still, waiting for the sergeant to give the signal.

She felt in her pocket for her tinderbox. What wouldn't they think of her now, those people in Middleborough? Turned her out of the church, they had, because she put on men's clothes. She knew because she had heard it being told around the campfire last week when a scout who came through said they were looking for a girl from Massachusetts who was rumored to have tried to join the Army. Think of it, a woman wearing breeches. Deborah had roared with laughter along with the rest of them, especially when they told the part about that girl borrowing some fellow's clothes, and when he found out he swore never to wear them again.

She felt a light touch on her elbow, the sign to begin snaking her way across the open area around the smokehouse. Pray God the window would not be too securely bolted. She knew the kind of window it would be, a wooden shutter, probably held by a leather thong inside, a window that could be easily opened for regulating the smoke. That was how the Thomas boys had stolen into the smokehouse to stuff their pockets with butts of bacon to toast over their campfires when they went hunting, with Deacon Thomas never the wiser.

She was proud of how quietly she could move, even over the scratchy gravel. Once she crawled over a pile of cow dung and wished she could rip out swear words as easily as the other soldiers did, but somehow the words wouldn't come, even in her mind.

She was at the window now. Across the yard she could faintly see a guard sitting against a tree, his musket over his knees. One of her party was creeping up behind him. She braced her foot against the shutter and pushed with all her muscle. The window gave way and fell to the dirt floor with a thud. Deborah squirmed into the opening like a nervous lizard and replaced the window after her.

The smokehouse was as dark as a well bottom.

Should she strike her light now and run the risk of having a telltale streak of it show around the window or should she make her cat's eyes work in the dark? No, it was better to work fast and dangerously with the candle.

She struck a spark with her flint, lit the candle, and goggled at the meat hanging from rafters and set on shelves. She pulled out her knife and cut down the hams, stacking them by the window. Then, working with frantic energy, she pushed the meat through the opening.

There was a shout from the Tories in the house.

"Set it on fire, Bobby. Grab your sack and run for it," whispered the sergeant.

Deborah lit the straw piled by the door, scattered it a bit, and wriggled out of the small window. She grabbed as many hams as she could. Behind her the smell of burning straw filled the air. Men with their arms full of meat were running with her, the fire serving to confuse the Tories as the sergeant had predicted. She paused a moment to gloat, and at that moment a shudder of pain that was far worse than all the pain she had ever imagined struck her. A musket ball had hit her thigh.

"Run for it! Bobby," shouted Ike, seeing her falter.

Deborah hung onto the hams in her arms, stumbled to the rendezvous, and picked up her musket. The men were loading the provisions on their backs.

"Bobby's been shot," said Ike. "We've got to help him get out of here."

"I can make it," said Deborah through gritted teeth.

She was hot and cold and faint, but she breathed deeply through her mouth and clenched her hands. She could feel the stream of blood running down her leg.

"The Tories are busy with their fire. We have two or three minutes start on them," said the sergeant. "If you can walk for a short spell, we'll carry you the rest of the way to the French camp and leave you there with the doctor."

It was nearly dawn when the sergeant and Ike carried her into the encampment and left her with the French doctor. The sleepy surgeon looked at the blood-stained tear in the breeches and laid Deborah on a pallet. She cried out with pain when he probed the spot gently.

"The ball ees there, but we'll let the lad rest a while before we take those breeches off and dig it out. Here, let the brandy ease the pain."

Deborah gratefully swallowed some brandy and closed her eyes, trying to keep her mind in focus. She must get out of here, crawl away and get herself to her cave where she could lie down in privacy and sleep a while. Then she could take the bullet out herself. She would rather die in any case than face detection in this French Army camp. Why had she thought she wanted to be a soldier? Courage, courage, she told herself.

She could hear the doctor's snores resume from his cot. Biting her lips to keep from crying out, she got herself on her feet. She took the bottle of brandy, and, cautiously, as the good woodsman she was, she got past the doctor, around the sentry, and into the woods as the first streaks of morning sun gave her the direction to follow to her cave.

In the cave were her woman's clean cloths. With her knife and the brandy and her tinderbox, canteen, and the butt of dried beef in her pocket she could hide and survive a week.

She drank a little water from her canteen when she crawled into her cave. She rested on her bed of leaves until her strength rose a little, then took off her breeches and washed the wound with cold water and brandy. She lit a candle from her tinderbox and passed the knife through the flame. Mistress Thomas had taught her that if you must cut a person, first burn the knife to cut the pain.

When the knife was cool, she steadied her hand, took a swallow of brandy, gritted her teeth hard, and, leaning against the rock for strength, she dug out the musket ball.

With her ears ringing, she leaned her head forward to keep from fainting, poured brandy on the wound again, stanched the blood with the clean cloth, and pressed hard on it. Sometimes conscious, sometimes faint, she kept the pressure on the spot until she fell over into a deep sleep. When she woke, her head was momentarily clear and the bleeding had subsided.

Sleeping and rousing, sometimes crying out with pain, Deborah woke after three days and felt her strength returning. Her head felt clear, and she ate some of the meat. She pulled herself with stubborn determination to the nearby spring, where she washed herself and her bandages and refilled her canteen.

Luckily the ball had landed in the fleshy part of her thigh, and the healing was quick. But a second, smaller, ball she discovered was deeply imbedded further down her leg. It was impossible to remove it. I shall keep it for a souvenir, she decided grimly as she moved painfully around the cave. In a few days she could return to the camp.

Ike was overjoyed to see her. "We heard you had run away from the French. I feared you were dead."

"I was out of my head, wandering in the woods," said Deborah.

"You did a good job on the raid," said Ike. "You lie here and I'll take care of you."

"I'm fine. I can do my duty as well as ever," lied Deborah when the doctor looked at her. The doctor dismissed her without an examination, pressed by sicker patients. But when, ten days later, she was ordered to another foray, her stomach flipped.

Tramp, tramp, tramp, how her leg hurt. She paid scant attention to Richard Snow, who was marching beside her. Suddenly Richard stumbled and fell, and lay writhing on the ground.

The corporal in charge halted the men. "He's terrible sick," he said. "He can't go forward, and we can't leave him behind."

"There's a house nearby. I could stay and look after him," volunteered Deborah.

"Good boy, Bobby. We have to keep moving or we'll all be targets in this Tory neighborhood. Good luck to you. Report back to headquarters when you get things under control."

Deborah, her leg on fire, dragged the desperately sick man to the nearest farmhouse. Old Mr. Van Tassel, the owner, let them in and grudgingly led them up to his bare attic.

"It's good enough for soldiers," he said meanly. "Ye can share it with the rats."

While Deborah rested her leg in the cold attic, she cared tenderly for Richard with the secret help of Van Tassel's daughter.

"My father is a strong Tory," she whispered. "He would not want it known that he is housing Patriot soldiers. All my father cares for is food for his belly."

"Give me some for mine," begged Deborah. "I am like to starve."

Miss Van Tassel covertly brought them food, water, and cover, but by the end of ten days poor Snow died. Deborah wrapped him in a blanket, said a prayer over his body, and let herself out of the locked garret by a knotted rope from the window.

The ten heartbreaking days had given her leg a chance to heal. She walked back to West Point ready for Army life again.

VIII

1783: The Treaty of Paris was signed in 1783.
Hostilities ceased on April 19, and the Army
was disbanded on November 3 of that year.

Except for a few Indian raids, the winter of 1783 was dull. In February the Colonel announced that all fighting would stop on April 19, exactly eight years since the first shot of the war was fired at Lexington. The peace treaty had been agreed upon in Paris, and the war was over. The Army, however, would remain together as a skeleton force until November.

One rainy morning as Deborah pulled herself up

from her straw mattress in the barracks the corporal brought her a summons from General Paterson. Her tongue stuck to the roof of her mouth, and her heart beat fast. Somehow wise General Paterson, whom she had only seen at a distance, had found out about her, and now she would be exposed and punished.

Ike stood there looking at her, a frown on his face. It was a mystery to all of them, lousy lowly foot soldiers that they were, why Bobby, who was never in trouble and did his job well, would be singled out for punishment. What else could it be but punishment?

Deborah washed herself and dusted off her uniform and dragged across the muddy drill field to the back door of the General's quarters.

"Take off your shoes," said the cook. "You can't be tracking mud into the General's house. He wants to see you in his office in the front of the house."

Deborah, sick with fright, followed the cook down the hall into a room where General Paterson himself sat by the fire with a tray of breakfast beside him.

"Can you serve a table and shave a face?" asked the General abruptly.

"Yes, sir," said Deborah in such a tone of relief that the General looked at her closely.

"It has simmered up to me that you are a well-mannered boy and gentle in your ways. Turn around and let me look at you. I am considering you for my personal waiter."

Deborah turned around, trying to look as soldierly

as possible without poking out her chest. She was jubilant with relief. To receive an honor instead of a court-martial was enough to buckle the knees with joy.

"He'll do," said the General to his aide, who was standing in the door. "See that he's washed and given a place to sleep in this house and issued decent new clothes. From now on you are my orderly, Shirtliff."

Deborah bade her comrades good-by and moved from the barracks to a small private attic room in the General's quarters. She fell into her daily routine of cleaning shoes, preparing special dishes, polishing swords and medals, and seeing to such details as clean handkerchiefs and mended stockings.

Mistress Paterson came to depend on Deborah so much that when word came in June that Deborah must return to her unit to march to Philadelphia, she was much annoyed with her husband for releasing his waiter.

"Bobby's military duty comes first," Deborah heard the General say crossly to his wife. "There can be no interfering."

Fifteen hundred soldiers were needed in Philadelphia to put down the revolt of disgruntled Pennsylvania troops who were rioting for back pay. They had threatened Congress with force.

A few years ago, Deborah would have given anything for a trip to Philadelphia, but now with her comfortable job in the General's house she dreaded getting into her marching boots.

"How come these soldiers need pay more than the rest of us?" grumbled Ike. "I don't get any pay."

"Neither do I. Seems to me that it's good enough that they feed us and give us uniforms and promise to pay us some day," said Deborah.

"General Washington himself gets no pay. I'd like money, but this isn't a wage earner's war. This is a war for, aw, you say it, Bobby. You talk better than I do," said the corporal.

"I don't know how to say it either, but if we had lost the war or never had it at all, then there wouldn't be any United States. As long as I can remember, people have been working to have a United States. I'm glad I got to help."

"That's well put," said Ike.

"Until the war is over and the British are gone, how's Congress going to raise money?" said the corporal. "They tried lotteries, and that didn't work very well." He hastened his step. "We've got to get to Philadelphia faster and put that insurrection down and show them that Massachusetts men don't need pay to make them good soldiers. Congress has got to figure out what to do about money. Why, they don't even circulate the Continental bills any more. I guess some people think Mr. Hancock can pull gold out of his cocked hat."

Thus they talked as they trudged to Philadelphia.

But the riot was over by the time the West Point soldiers arrived, for General Washington had dealt quickly with the mutiny. Deborah spent two days wandering the streets of Philadelphia sightseeing in the time alloted them before they were to march back to West Point. She didn't feel very good; no doubt it was due to the heat. She stood and stared up at the Liberty Bell. She felt dizzy, and her breakfast rose to her throat. She sat down on the curb, and to her chagrin vomited and then fainted. When she came to, a doctor was standing over her saying to an orderly, "This soldier has the malignant fever. Take him to the hospital before we spread any more cases."

The hospital! That was where you went to die. In spite of her weak protest, two men carried her there on a stretcher.

"We have no beds left," said the matron when they entered the hospital door.

"Here's one, Madam Parker," called an attendant. "This fellow over here just died. We can move out the body and put him in here."

Deborah was too sick to object. That was the last thing she remembered as she lay for days racked with the fever. Once she had a moment of consciousness when she pleaded with the doctor and the matron to move her from the dead soldier's bunk.

"Poor fellow," said Madam Parker kindly. "Let us humor him, Doctor Binney. Alas, there is a new vacancy this morning in the third-floor loft."

Jones, the orderly, moved her to the third floor. The next morning Deborah had a half-lucid moment. She was too weak to speak, but she could hear the undertakers talking through the mist of semi-consciousness.

"This here one's done for," said one of them. "We'll haul him away next. This time I get the shirt and boots, and the breeches and coat are yours. You got the first choice on the last corpse."

"I did not. You did," argued the other.

Abject horror seized Deborah. They had come to bury her! They were talking about dividing her clothes, their only pay for taking away her body to potter's field. The shock was enough to give her a last weak burst of life.

I'm alive, I'm alive, the words kept flitting through her mind, but she could not catch them and make them come out on her tongue.

"Hush your quarreling," said Jones sharply to the undertakers. "Have you no respect for the dead? Get out until I send for you."

All the power and energy that Deborah could force came to her throat.

Glug, she articulated.

"What was that?" Jones turned around and looked at Deborah. She was the only patient left in the room, for the others had all died, and the bodies had been removed.

But Deborah could not muster the strength to make another sound.

"Doctor Binney," called Jones. "Maybe I'm hearing things, but I could swear this corpse made a noise."

Doctor Binney puffed up the narrow stairs to look at the patient. The noise was probably a rat in the wall, but a doctor had to be sure.

"Shirtliff?" said the doctor, putting his mouth close to Deborah's ear.

Once again Deborah concentrated her whole will to live into making one sound.

"As God lives, he did make a noise!" cried Doctor Binney. "Quick, Jones, run below and get my medicine bag!"

Doctor Binney tore open the soldier's coat, ripped the shirt open, raised an eyebrow at the linen binder under the shirt, and tore it off to feel the heart.

"Matron, Madam Parker," cried the doctor in such agitation that the matron fairly flew up the stairs, "we have just pulled a soldier literally back from the grave, and *he* is a *female!*"

Jones panted back up the stairs with the bag of drugs.

"That will be all, Jones. Madam Parker will help me." Doctor Binney forced brandy down Deborah's throat, and Madam Parker and he massaged Deborah's arms and legs until her pulse began to throb faintly. They looked at each other over Deborah's body.

"Don't tell a soul until I decide what to do," said the flabbergasted doctor.

"Let me take her to my apartment and nurse her there," said the bewildered matron. "This is the only soldier of this type I am ever likely to see."

When Deborah passed the crisis of the fever and

came to in Madam Parker's apartment some days later, she looked at her clean bed and her white nightshirt. She expected the first words from the matron and the doctor to be accusations and questions.

But neither of them made any mention of her sex. Hour after hour, Deborah lay in her bed pondering the situation. On the day that she was allowed to dress and stand on her feet, she asked for her uniform, and Madam Parker brought it to her all cleaned and mended and ready to wear.

"The doctor is going to take you to his own home," she said. "He often does this until a soldier is strong enough to rejoin his unit."

She brushed away Deborah's thanks and warned her to be careful of her health during her recovery.

Deborah moved into Doctor Binney's house. He introduced her to his motherly wife and his three pretty teen-age daughters as a gallant Continental soldier. The girls outdid themselves taking Bobby for picnics in the woods, sailing on the Delaware, and to musicales in Philadelphia's rich and fashionable society.

"Papa must like you very much," said the youngest and prettiest of the Misses Binney. "He never before let us go anywhere without some tiresome old relative along."

"Perhaps your father trusts me more than others," said Deborah manfully. "I think your father is a very kind and remarkable man."

Deborah recovered too fast for her own pleasure. What wonderful days these were with the new awareness of the joy of being alive. At night she buried her head in her pillow, laughing at the girls who tried to flirt with her.

One morning in early fall, when her cheeks at last were pink and her step was full of bounce, Doctor Binney sent for her to come to his office.

"Bobby, do you have a particular friend in your company, some soldier who shares your confidences?"

"No, sir. I have no close friends," said Deborah.

"It is time for you to return to your company. Yours has been an interesting case, Shirtliff. I have been trying to decide what to do about you, and I think the time has come for you to face the music, as the saying goes."

Deborah's knees felt weak. So it was coming now, the revealing denunciation. But instead, Doctor Binney reached in his desk and drew out a sealed letter.

"I want you to give this to General Paterson himself on your return to West Point. Be careful of your health and continue to be as discreet in everything as you have been true to the cause of freedom. When you have received your discharge from the Army, send me a written sketch of your life."

Doctor Binney and the entire family saw Bobby off at the stage office. Deborah was almost speechless with gratitude when the good man paid her fare all the way to West Point.

Deborah reached West Point in early October with the letter safely in her pocket. The definitive Treaty of

Paris had been signed by Great Britain, Spain, France, and the United States on September 3, 1783, and the third day of November had been set for the formal disbanding of the Army of the United States. Many of the men had already gone home to cut wood for the winter and to sit by their firesides, spinning tales of the war.

Ike was still there. He gave a whoop of pleasure when he saw Deborah, clean and healthy, walk into the barracks.

"Why, here's Bobby, back from the dead. Oh, how we grieved for you, lad."

Bobby was the center of attention as she told of being almost buried alive. If only she could have told them the whole story, how their eyes would have bugged out. Then she thought uncomfortably of the letter in her coat pocket. Did Doctor Binney write the whole story to General Paterson?

The next morning, Deborah presented herself to General Paterson's quarters, gave the letter to his aide, and went back to join the wood-cutting force as she had been ordered to do.

Deborah was loading logs onto the sledge when a messenger came into the woods and found her. "General Paterson wants to see you at once," he panted. "He says to come to his home, and he will receive you without delay. I guess he wants you back as his orderly, and right now."

Deborah ran all the way. She knocked at the back door.

"General Paterson has almost got the apoplexy.

What have you done?" said the cook. "He said to bring you to his study at once."

Deborah knocked on the General's door. This was *it*.

"Sit down," ordered the General.

To sit in the presence of the General, lowly private that she was, was unthinkable. Deborah dusted off her breeches and perched gingerly on the edge of the chair. The letter lay open on his desk.

"Can it be true?" the General said in amazement, staring at Deborah. "Are you a female?"

Suddenly Deborah was on the floor, on her knees. For the first time in her Army life, she could let the tears come freely.

"Please, sir, have mercy. Don't be hard on me. I only wanted to serve my country and see the world, and there was no other way a woman could do it. I never misbehaved myself once. You can ask anybody. Nobody but yourself and Doctor Binney knows that I am not a man. I promise you that." Poor Deborah knelt in a sobbing heap on the carpet, her face hidden in her hands.

"Get up, Bobby, or whatever your name is. Nobody is going to punish you. Why, I have respect for you, my —girl," gasped the flustered General.

And then the General put his head in his hands and laughed until Deborah, in spite of her watery eyes, laughed uncertainly with him.

"What shall we do? I can't send you back to the barracks again, Miss—what is your name?"

"Sampson, sir. Deborah Sampson, from Middleborough, Massachusetts."

"This is truly theatrical," said the General. "There's little enough to cheer the troops these days. I want you to ask my wife to come here. She'll lend you a dress, and then we'll see who recognizes you."

The shaken Mistress Paterson led 'Bobby' to her bedroom, where with the help of an astonished maidservant, Deborah undressed, washed, curled her hair, and put on the General's wife's dress. Mistress Paterson had to sit down on the side of the bed to control her agitation when the serving girl reported that the General had sent for Colonel Jackson, who was now waiting below to meet the Patersons' bewitching visitor.

"Mistress Paterson, I am more afraid now than I ever was in my breeches," said Deborah, holding back and touching her hostess with an icy hand.

"You have to do what the General says," reminded Mistress Paterson. "I suppose you're still in the Army."

Mistress Paterson was seized with a fit of coughing when Colonel Jackson stood up and bowed to Miss Deborah Sampson. Deborah sat demurely in her chair, her face red with a legitimate blush.

"Don't you recognize the young lady, Colonel?" asked the General jovially.

"How could I ever forget so charming a face?" said the Colonel gallantly.

Deborah kept her eyes down, wishing she were dead.

"You're sure you don't recognize her, Colonel? She has another name, Private Robert Shirtliff, one of your men."

For Deborah, it was as bad as the shock of being

under gunfire. The General and the Colonel were so flustered, they were incoherent, their composure gone, their military manners shaken. Whatever I expected, it was not like this, thought Deborah dizzily. However, the two men thought up a punishment that made Deborah turn weak-kneed.

"Come, Miss Sampson, we're going to inspect the troops now and see who recognizes you," said the General.

Deborah walked shyly between the two officers.

"Summon the entire company," ordered the General. "Ask the men to pass in review before a distinguished visitor."

The ragged soldiers marched before the elegant lady.

"Order parade rest," said the General. "Men," said the General informally, "this is a unique occasion. I am going to present to you Miss Deborah Sampson, better known to you as Private Bobby Shirtliff."

Deborah wished she could have been invisible in the barracks to hear what the men said later, but the General whisked her away to his house, where he put her in the care of Mistress Paterson.

On the twenty-fifth of October, Deborah received her honorable discharge, signed by General Knox. Deborah examined the paper.

"When I was a little girl," she told the Patersons, "a dear friend of mine brought me a book of GULLIVER's TRAVELS. He bought the book from General Henry Knox, who at that time was a bookseller in Boston."

"I daresay your travels would be as interesting as those of Gulliver," said the General. He handed her good-conduct testimonials signed by himself, General Shepherd, and Colonel Jackson.

"What are you going to do now, Miss Sampson?" asked Mistress Paterson.

"I am going back to Plymouth tomorrow to make my peace with my mother," said Deborah. "Then I will decide what to do next."

"Will you go by stage?" asked the youngest Paterson boy, who regarded Deborah as something not quite real.

"I suppose I will," said Deborah, "but before I go to bed I want to thank all of you for being so kind to me."

That night Deborah looked at the beautiful travel dress that Mistress Paterson had lent her for the trip home. In a box under her bed was her uniform. How easy it was to travel as a foot soldier, how free to hop on the back of a farmer's cart. She hung Mistress Paterson's dress on a peg with a note of thanks, put on her old uniform, and slipped out the kitchen door.

There was one good-by she had to say. At midnight she tiptoed into the barracks where Ike lay sleeping. She shook him awake and put her finger over his mouth to quiet him.

"Good-by, Ike. It's Bobby. I'm going home now. Thank you for being a good friend to me."

"Is it true that you're a girl, Bobby? Here you are back in your regimentals," whispered the mystified Ike.

"I'm a girl, all right," said Deborah. "I just put

these on until I get home. Good luck in the Ohio Territory. I heard you plan to go there."

"Thankee, Bobby. You fooled all of us. If I were a married man, I could have told my grandchildren that I served with a female soldier."

Deborah slipped out into the night and headed for Plymouth. A strange woman was at the door at Uncle Nehemiah's house. Deborah's heart contracted. Was Mother dead? Such a possibility had never crossed her mind.

"Mr. Nehemiah Bradford is dead," said the woman. "His sister, Madam Sampson, has moved to the other side of town to live with a married daughter. You wouldn't be that son Ephraim that she spoke of? No?"

The woman stared after Deborah. She had heard a strange story about Madam Sampson, how she had a daughter who, the rumor went, had tried to join the Army and had been put out of the church for wearing men's clothes. Some said she had killed herself and some said she had really joined the Army. Oh well, some people would believe anything.

Deborah opened the door to Hannah's kitchen. Mother, with her newest grandchild on her lap, and Sylvia, who was setting the board for supper, and Hannah, plump and matronly, bustling around the kitchen, all looked up.

"Eph!" cried Mother. "Is that you, Eph?"

Deborah just stood there, unable to speak, it was so good to see them again.

NEW-YORK,
January 10.

An extraordinary instance of virtue in a *female soldier*, has occurred lately in the American army, in the Massachusetts line, viz. a lively, comely young nymph, 19 years of age, dressed in man's apparal has been discovered; and what redounds to her honor, she has served in the character of a soldier for near three years undiscovered; during which time she displayed herself with activity, alertness, chastity and valour, having been in several skirmishes with the enemy, and received two wounds; a small shot remaining in her to this day, she was a remarkable vigilant soldier on her post, and always gained the admiration and applause of her officers; was never found in liquor, and always kept company with the most upright and temperate soldiers: For several months this gallantress served with credit as a waiter in a General officer's family; a violent illness, (when the troops were at Philadelphia) led to the discovery of her sex; she has since, been honorably discharged from the army with a reward, and sent to her connexions, who, it appears live to the Eastward of Boston, at a place called Munduncook. The cause of her personating a man, it is said, proceeded from the rigour of her parents, who exerted their prerogative, to induce her marriage with a young man she had conceived a great antipathy for, together with her being a remarkable heroine, and warmly attached to the cause of her country, in the service of which, it must be acknowledged, she gained reputation; and no doubt, will be noticed by the compilers of the history of our grand revolution. She passed by the name of Robert Shurtlieff, while in the army, and was borne on the rolls of the regiment as such:—For particular reasons her real name is withheld, but the facts aforementioned are unquestionable and unembellished—

Yesterday arrived the schooner Renown, Archibald Campbell, master, in 24 days from Jamaica.

And on Thursday last, a transport ship at Sandy-Hook, in five months from England.

country people and buried. For the honor of a country man, I must mention, that he found two guineas and a half in the pocket of the midshipman, which he brought on board to the Commodore—We sail to-morrow if the wind is fair."

The following are the names of the truly unfortunate Gentlemen, alluded to in the foregoing letter.

First Lieut. of the ship, the hon. Hamilton Douglass Hallyburton, second son of the Earle of Morton.

Lieut. of marines, James Champion.

Robert Haywood, Charles Gascoinge, Willam Spry, George Towers, George Faddy, William Scott, David Reddie, Alexander Johnston, } Midshipmen.

Who were found the 2d January, and buried on Sandy-Hook island.

Robert Wood, midshipman, found 2d Jan. and buried by the country people.

John Mc. Chain, seamen, found and buried by the La Sophia's seamen the 2d' Jan.

MISSING.

Andrew Hamilton, } Midshipmen.
William Tomlinson, }

☞ *The piece proposing a mode to facilitate the circulation of news-papers in the country, on account of its length must be deferred till our next.*

On the 2d of last month, the Assembly of Virginia passed an Act, for declaring who shall be Citizens of that Commonwealth: The following is the particular enacting Clause:

BE it enacted, That all free persons, born within the territory of this Commonwealth, except as hereafter excepted; all persons, not being natives, who have obtained a right to citizenship under the said act; and all children, wheresoever born, whose

An account of Deborah's army career which appeared in the *New York Independent Gazette* of January 10, 1789.

Hannah dropped her stirring spoon and let out a shriek. "Mother, it's Deborah! Don't you see? It's Deborah herself."

Hannah grabbed the baby from Mother, who had turned white and trembled so that she seemed about to faint. Deborah ran across the kitchen and knelt in front of Mother. She pulled off her Army cap and put her face on her mother's lap.

"Don't you know me? I'm Deborah, all right. I'm back from the war."

Mother wouldn't admit it was Deborah until Hannah and Sylvia had dressed their sister in women's clothes. Deborah sat at the table with them, filling up on savory food and family news.

Jonny, Elisha, and Eph were all discharged from the Army now. The older boys were married and had children. Nehemiah was apprenticed in Boston.

Deborah herself answered the questions that Hannah's husband and Sylvia, tall and beautiful at seventeen, kept asking her until she begged for sleep.

IX

1784–1827: The Constitution of the United States was adopted on July 2, 1788.

George Washington became the first President of the United States on April 30, 1789.

In the next decades, under the Presidencies of John Adams, Thomas Jefferson, James Madison, James Monroe, and John Quincy Adams, the United States expanded and took its place as a strong nation with a two-party system.

April 7, 1784: Deborah Sampson of Middleborough and Benjamin Gannett of Sharon were married at the home of Mr. Gannett's father in Sharon, Massachusetts.

Deborah, Mother, and Sylvia slept in a bed so small that by morning Deborah had made up her mind that this house was too crowded for her.

"Deborah, you know we're glad you're back alive, but you've shamed us," said Hannah. "Promise you won't wear those breeches again."

"I probably won't need to wear them again, but I can't say I'm sorry I did. Hannah, I'm thinking of start-

ing out in a new place." Her family would never understand her.

"Why don't you go to Aunt Alice in Stoughton?
Her husband, Uncle Waters, is a broad-minded type. I
think he would gladly take you in until you decide what
to do. It mortifies Mother that you were in the Army and
were put out of the Church."

At the week's end, Deborah was established in
Stoughton. Uncle Waters regarded Deborah as his own
creation, inviting his friends in to sit respectfully by the
winter fire and see for themselves the female soldier.

One of them was Benjamin Gannett from Sharon, a
mild-mannered man of thirty with a quiet sense of humor,
who sat in the Waters' kitchen listening to Deborah and
her uncle, who kept up a never-ending lot of banter. Mr.
Gannett joined in. He and Uncle Waters thought it
would be hilarious if Deborah would put on the old
uniform and try to charm the girls of the neighborhood, but Deborah refused. Mr. Gannett dropped in
again and again.

"I have to find out more about this fighting," he
said with a twinkle in his eye. "I didn't see much of it
myself, being only in the local militia. I had to stay home
and run the farm for my old parents."

"I love a farm," said Deborah. "I like a farm better
than any battlefield or big city, but I guess nobody will
ever believe that."

"I believe it," said Mr. Gannett. "I can believe anything you say, Miss Sampson. I think you're incredible,

Benjamin and Deborah Gannett's home in Sharon, Massachusetts.

meaning by that that I consider you a most extraordinary person. I would like to show you my farm."

On the first fine March day, Mr. Gannett arrived at the Waters' door astride his farm horse, leading another mount.

" 'Tis a good day to ride over my farm," he said.

Deborah stopped her spinning for Aunt Alice and put on her cloak and tied her kerchief on her head. She jumped on the spare horse, riding astride as she used to do at the Thomas' farm. As they rode the five miles to the Gannett farm, the spring wind turned Deborah's face rosy.

173

"I love your farm!" she cried after they had galloped over the acres.

"How would you like to share it with me, Deborah?" he asked.

"I would like that more than anything in the world, Benjamin," said Deborah.

Not that she asked their opinion, but Uncle Waters and Aunt Alice approved.

"It takes an extraordinary man to marry such an extraordinary female," Uncle Waters said. "And I think Benjamin Gannett is just such a man."

Deborah married Benjamin Gannett on the seventh day of April, 1784, at the Gannett house in Sharon. She wove herself a white wool dress and embroidered it with red leaves.

Two years later, their first child, Earl, was born, followed by Mary, three years later, and by Patience the next year. Happy and busy as a wife and mother, she sometimes saw her old friends from Middleborough. Mistress Thomas, now a cheerful grandmother, sat in Deborah's kitchen one day.

"I can't believe you really fought in that war, Deborah," she said. Deborah was making cheese and trying to keep little Mary from falling in the tub.

"It's no harder to fight in a war than to run a farm kitchen, I sometimes think," said Deborah. "I scarcely have time to keep up with the news, I am that busy. But it seems to me that the country is running smoothly now that General Washington is President and we have a Constitution."

"You always had more of a head for politics and news than any woman I ever knew, Deborah," said Mistress Thomas, rising to go. "I wish you could visit me more often, but I know you are busy with all the things you do and your leg hurting as it does."

It was true, her leg did hurt. It hurt until she was often unable to help Benjamin on the farm, and there was no money for a hired man or for special occasions like Christmas, which was coming soon. The Gannett family, like many others, had got away from the Puritan custom of ignoring Christmas. It was an increasingly festive season now. If only she had a little money, she might buy some gifts.

Many of the Massachusetts soldiers were collecting back pay now. I deserve it as much as the men, Deborah decided, putting down the newspaper she was reading. She had Colonel Jackson's good-conduct certificate in her trunk, and she knew that Captain Thorpe was living up at Dedham now. He would write a testimonial that he had enrolled her that day at Bellingham. She had plenty of proof that she had actually seen service, including her limp.

Captain Thorpe sent her an enlistment certificate with a letter of good wishes, and Deborah sat down by the lamp that evening on the eleventh of January, 1792, and with Benjamin's advice wrote to the Legislature of the Commonwealth of Massachusetts. "To His Excellency the Governor, the Honourable Senate, and the Honourable House of Representatives, in General Court Assembled, this Eleventh day of January 1792.

Boston. Augt 1, 1786

This may Certify that Robert Shurtliff was a Soldier in my Regiment in the Continental army for the town of Uxbridge in the Commonwealth of Massachusetts & was inlisted for the term of three years — That he had the confidence of his officers and did his duty as a faithful & good Soldier, & was honorably discharged the army of the United States

Henry Jackson late Col in the
American army —

Whom it may concern

A true copy of the original delivered said Shurtliff

Attest —
John Avery jun^r Sec^y

The Secretary of the Commonwealth of Massachusetts

Deborah's good-conduct certificate signed by Colonel Henry Jackson.

The Memorial of Deborah Gannett

Humbly Sheweth that your Memorialist from Zeal for the good of her Country was induc'd, and by the name of Robert Shirtliff did on May 20, 1782, Inlist as a Soldier in the Continental Service for Three Years, into the 4th Regiment, Col. Shepherd's (afterwards Col. Jackson's) in Capt. George Webb's Compy. & was muster'd at Worcester, by Capt. Eliphalet Thorpe of Dedham, the 23rd of the same Month & went to the Camp, under the Command of Sergeant Gambel & was faithful and constant in doing Duty, with other Soldiers, and was engag'd with the enemy at Tarry Town New York & was wounded there by the Enemy, & continued in Service untill discharg'd, by General Knox at West Point, October 25, 1783. —— Your Memorialist has made some application to receive pay for her services in the Army, but being a Female, & not knowing the proper steps to be taken to get pay for her services, has hitherto not receiv'd one farthing for her services: whether it has been occasion'd by the fault of Officers in making up the Rolls, or whether Effrican Hamlin paymaster to the 4th regiment, has carried off the papers, &c, your Memorialist cannot say: but your Memorialist prays this Honourable Court to consider the Justness of her Claim, & Grant her pay as a good soldier; and your Memorialist as in Duty bound shall ever pray.

Deborah Gannett"

Ten days later, Benjamin came in from town with the latest *Massachusetts Spy* in his hand. "You're written about in the paper, my girl," he said to Deborah.

Together they pored over the column of the "Proceedings of the Legislature of Massachusetts". FEMALE HEROISM it was entitled.

"I would say they will no doubt pay you some money," said Benjamin. A few weeks later Deborah re-

A copy of Deborah's enlistment certificate sent to her
by Captain Eliphalet Thorpe.

ceived thirty-four pounds back pay and a letter with Governor Hancock's bold signature at the bottom.

There was a flurry of talk in Sharon about Deborah's collecting the pay. Deborah smiled at some of the distorted stories that had grown up about her, but it was good to have the money. Now she could pay the doctor for the many times he had given her medicine to ease the pain in her leg. More often people forgot that she was ever in the war and spoke of her only as a kind and capable neighbor in times of trouble.

When Mistress Susannah Shepherd died in childbirth in September of 1796 leaving a motherless infant, Deborah took the baby, Susanna, home with her. Deborah rocked the tiny thing by the fire while Mary, Earl, and Patience looked over her shoulder.

"Benjamin," said Deborah, "I want to keep this baby for our own."

"Deborah, Deborah, your heart is too big. How can we take another mouth to feed?" said Benjamin.

"Oh, Father, please, please," begged Mary and Patience, who were six and seven now. "We'll take care of the baby."

Benjamin Gannett sighed. Sometimes it was hard being married to a woman whose heart seemed to encompass the needs of the whole world. Earl, who was now ten, looked at his family of sisters.

"I wish it were a boy," he said.

"We take what God sends. I think God sent us this baby to keep. We'll manage to feed her somehow. Even though I am not a member of any church and am criticized for reading Thomas Paine's *Age of Reason*, I recognize God's will."

"Why don't you look out the window, Mother, as you tell us to do. Maybe you'll think of a way out there."

"I'll do that," said Deborah. "It has never failed me yet."

Deborah handed the baby to Benjamin to hold and walked over to the window. There was a man coming up the walk. Deborah opened the door.

"Mistress Gannett, I am Herman Mann. I have come to see you on a matter of business."

Deborah invited the strange man into the house. He

settled down in the best chair and cleared his throat. "Mistress Gannett, I have heard of your exploits as a soldier. I am a newspaperman, being engaged at present with THE VILLAGE REGISTER in Dedham. I want to write a book about you. I can arrange for a list of subscribers to pay the costs, and there will be money for us both from the book sales. I will write the book. You just give me a few hints, and I will make it like a book of fiction."

Deborah looked questioningly at her husband.

Benjamin patted the baby, who was lying quietly on his lap. "Suit yourself, Deborah. How can I say no to the book or the baby because providence seems to decree that the book will pay for the baby!"

Mary and Patience shouted with such joy that little Susanna woke with a wail. The book wasn't nearly as interesting as the baby.

"I'm glad you agree, Benjamin," said Deborah, smiling at Benjamin, who was soothing the baby. "Did you know, children, that your father's name means 'beloved'?" Benjamin gave her a happy life.

Herman Mann came many times to the Gannett house while Deborah, tending baby Susanna, reminisced over war experiences.

"I have put it in that you were at the Battle of Yorktown," said Mr. Mann.

"That's not the exact truth," said Deborah.

"We mean this to be interesting, don't we? It becomes more interesting if we can work in the events of Cornwallis' surrender."

"It's true I used to spin stories and say I was there," laughed Deborah. "All soldiers tell tall tales."

Mr. Joseph Stone of Framingham came to Sharon to paint her picture, surrounded by flags and patriotic symbols. Deborah had a new dress for the occasion, white lawn with a high-waisted blue sash and a ruffled collar. Her hair was curled down over her shoulders in the latest style, and she wore a string of choker beads.

"Deborah, you are a downright fashion plate," declared Benjamin, looking at her with pride. He examined the small painting, four inches by five inches in size, painted in oil on paper to save the cost of canvas. "Your face looks better in real life than it does in the picture. I wouldn't say it does you justice."

But the children were very proud. Not many people had real portraits painted and put in a book to boot.

In 1796, the year before John Adams became the second President, THE FEMALE REVIEW was published. Deborah held the book in her hand and read the awesome title page aloud to the children.

"THE FEMALE REVIEW OR MEMOIRS OF AN AMERICAN YOUNG LADY
Whose Life And Character Are Peculiarly Distinguished — Being a Continental Soldier For Nearly Three Years, In The Late American War.
During Which Time
She Performed The Duties Of Every Department Into Which She Was Called With Punctual Exactness, Fidelity And Honor, And Preserved Her Chastity Inviolate, By The Most Artful Concealment Of Her Sex."

THE FEMALE REVIEW

LIFE OF

DEBORAH SAMPSON

THE FEMALE SOLDIER

IN THE

War of the Revolution

WITH

AN INTRODUCTION AND NOTES

BY

JOHN ADAMS VINTON

Boston
J. K. WIGGIN & WM. PARSONS LUNT
M DCCC LXVI

Paula Phillips

Facsimile of the cover of *The Female Review.*

On the opposite page was an engraving of the portrait.

"How do you like it?" beamed Mr. Mann. He rubbed his fingers appreciatively over the leather cover of a second copy.

"Give me a chance to read it first," said Deborah. "But I'll admit the cover is nice."

Deborah was disturbed with what lay between the covers. Mr. Mann had made so many mistakes that she reproached him.

"Then some day I must write a better one," he agreed.

"Write it and then you can publish it after I die," said Deborah. "I can't get my housework done with people tramping in here day and night to look at me and ask me silly questions. I'm a thirty-seven-year-old woman with four children to look after, and I have not the time to spend being a freak."

One of the visitors who stopped by to talk about the book was Mr. Paul Revere. Deborah had often seen him pass the house on his way to and from his prosperous copper works in Canton. Everybody knew Mr. Revere, and now it seemed that everybody knew Mrs. Gannett. Mr. Revere accepted a cool drink of water from the well and rested his horse while he and Deborah talked about the war.

With all the notoriety THE FEMALE REVIEW didn't bring in as much money as Mr. Mann had predicted, Deborah realized sadly. By 1802 Benjamin was sick, and Deborah was unable to do much farm work. She stood one day looking out the window. Surely there must be some way for her to earn some more money. People were still coming by the house to ask about her experiences. Why not hire a hall and charge for it, she thought in a moment of inspiration.

Without consulting Benjamin this time, she wrote Mr. Mann and made the suggestion. He could advise her, perhaps help her. Mr. Mann arrived in Sharon several days later, wildly enthusiastic about the idea.

"My dear Mrs. Gannett, I will be your manager," he cried. "We can both get rich from this. I myself will write your oration and provide a uniform for you and make all the arrangements."

With Patience and Mary now old enough to look after Susanna and their father, and Earl, now sixteen, able to manage the farm, Deborah studied her itinerary and prepared to set out. Never before to her knowledge had a woman made a tour to give talks for money. Not only would she give her speech in uniform, but she would go through the manual of arms, which she had not forgotten.

In March of 1802, Deborah packed her bag and put a blank diary in her purse for recording expenses and experiences. The speech was memorized, a poor meaningless lot of words in her own estimation, but Mr. Mann assured her that this was the sort of thing one said at an oration. She would make her first appearance in Boston.

At the Liberty Square rooming house of Mr. Robert

Williams, Deborah dressed in her newly tailored uniform and went by carriage to the Federal Street Theater, where she would make her speech. She smiled, remembering the last time she was in Boston, twenty years ago, when she slept in the stable with the other grooms in mortal dread that someone would find out that she was a girl.

The three Boston lectures were such a success that she never found time to write the details in her diary, but the newspapers recorded it. Deborah went home at the week's end with three copies of the *Columbian Centinal* in her bag. Her speech had been advertised in the papers on March 20, 24, and 27. The children pored over them, half embarrassed by their famous mother.

In May she went to Providence, where she wrote in her diary after speaking in Amidon Hall. [sic.]

May 5 . . . When I entred the Hall I must say I was much pleased at the appearence of the audience. it appreared from almost every countenence that they were full of unbelieff—I mean in Reguard to my being the person that served in the Reavolutionary Army.

Some of them which I happened to overhear Swore that I was a lad of not more than Eighteen years of age. . . .

May 8 . . . Rode from Providence to Boston. Sunday I was very sick of Distetary. at 5 o'clock I took five of Dr. Andossen's pill which appeared to have no effect in Reguard to afford me the least Releaf.

10 . . . On Monday morning I took a large Dose of castor oil which had a tendency to Releave me.

13 . . . came home to Sharon.

DEBORAH
SAMPSON
GANNETT
WOMAN SOLDIER IN THE WAR OF THE
REVOLUTION·ENLISTED UNDER THE NAME
OF ROBERT SHURTLEFF·SEVERAL YEARS
IN ACTIVE SERVICE·WOUNDED IN THE
BATTLE OF TARRYTOWN·HONORABLY
DISCHARGED IN 1783·PENSIONED BY
CONGRESS IN 1805
THIS TABLET IS PLACED HERE
BY REQUEST OF HER GRANDSON
GEORGE WASHINGTON GAY

Paula Phillips

Close-up of tablet which is part of a Civil War memorial erected by the town of Sharon in Rock Ridge Cemetery in 1906 from bequests left by George Washington
Gay and his wife Eunice Lyon Gay. The memorial
tablet to Deborah was included at the request of Mr.
Gay who was Deborah's grandson.

186

For a year Deborah traveled and lectured, returning home frequently between engagements. Sometimes she was homesick. In September she wrote in her diary:

"O Dear, Could I but once more see my three dear children! Why do I say 3? Have I forgotten my Dear little Susanna Shepperd!"

In November she arrived in Lisle, New York, where she stayed with old friends, the Patersons. The General, now Judge Paterson, and his lady met Deborah at the stage station. Mistress Paterson kissed Deborah on the cheek and stood back to look at her.

"And to think that you were the well-mannered waiter who once served my husband! How handsome you are, Bobby, Mrs. Gannett, I mean. I call you by the new *Mrs.* instead of the old fashioned *Mistress* because you look so modern and fashionable."

Deborah visited with them for nearly a month. Judge Paterson was campaigning for a seat in Congress.

"Come, ladies, ride with me while I go vote gathering," invited the Judge. "My old soldier friend here should attract plenty of attention."

Deborah laughed and climbed into the carriage beside Mistress Paterson while they rode around the countryside.

"If I'm elected I'll see what I can do for pensions for old soldiers, including you, Mrs. Gannett," he promised. "With Mr. Jefferson as President now, I'm sure fairness will be done."

"I've done enough traveling and talking," said Deborah when she returned to her family in August, 1803. Her pocketbook was filled, she had the prospect of a pension, and she had tales to tell the family about her stops in Holden, Massachusetts, where she visited her old Captain George Webb of Army days; and in Brookfield, Northampton, Worcester, Springfield, and Boston in Massachusetts. She went to Rhode Island as well, seeing Providence and Newport, and over to New York where she visited Albany, Schenectady, Ballston Springs, Lisle, and other places.

Mary and Patience took turns trying on their mother's new bonnet. "Be careful of it," said Deborah, "I paid two dollars for it, as you'll see on my expense list. Oh, the money I had to spend. Of course I had to have my hair dressed before every performance. Sometimes it cost as much as fifty cents. Prices get higher all the time."

The air was full of pension talk. The Federal Government had voted funds for the veterans, Deborah discovered. In the fall, after Deborah had returned from her tour, Mr. Revere stopped by to pay his respects.

"I will gladly write a letter in your behalf," he told her when she mentioned that she planned to apply for the new Federal pension.

One February day he returned to show her a copy of the letter he had written to Mr. William Eustis, a member of Congress from Massachusetts. Mr. Revere was a good man who could be counted on and whose name bore weight.

In 1805 Deborah was placed on a list of invalid soldiers and granted a pension of forty-eight dollars a with back pay dating to January 1, 1803. Whe pocketed the money she thought back to the dreadful when she removed the musket ball from her leg. If on the second one could have been taken out at the same time, she might not be an invalid today. The money was not a real compensation, but it was good for her soul, she decided, that the government had rewarded her the same as a man, proving that a woman could serve her country and be recognized for it. In 1818, following Madison's term and while Monroe was President, when all the Federal pensions were enlarged, Deborah's pension was handled like all the others.

Deborah and Benjamin lived quietly at the farm. The children married, and there were twelve grandchildren in and out of the house. Deborah held the little ones on her knee and told them stories.

"Why do you always tell them so many outrageous tales?" asked Sylvia, now Mrs. Cushman, who was visiting Deborah one April day in 1827.

"Stories make them strong," said Deborah. "If Grandmère had not told me about Joan of Arc, and if Cousin Fuller hadn't told me the Bible story of Deborah in such an exciting fashion, I might not have known that women can do strong things. And if Mr. Conant hadn't given me the book about Gulliver's travels, I might not have been so keen about seeing new sights. Without hero tales, children might never find the courage to try strong deeds themselves. We need courage and strong deeds from girls as well as boys in our new country. You might not believe me, sister, but I learned things that made me live a happier life with my husband and children and neighbors just by reading the works of William Shakespeare."

"You always say such different things, Deborah. But I'm proud of you. Even Mother was proud of you by the time she died, but she always felt bad about your being put out of the Church. But things have changed now. These modern children don't learn the Puritan Catechism any more."

"I never taught it to mine," said Deborah. "But one teaching from my childhood stayed with me. Do you remember the little verse we used to say about looking out the window? I've looked out the window all my life, looking for something, I'm not sure what. Sylvia, I don't think I have much more life to live."

"Oh, Deborah, don't say such a thing," said Sylvia.

"It's true," said Deborah. "After I die my pension will stop, and I don't know how Benjamin will manage. He has been a good husband to me, and we have been happy. I left instructions with Mr. Mann that after I die he can publish the new version of the FEMALE REVIEW. That money can go to Benjamin, or maybe Benjamin can get a pension, as widows do. John Quincy Adams is a good President with the veterans' interests at heart."

190

Paula Phillips

Deborah Gannett's gravestone in Rock Ridge Cemetery, Sharon, Massachusetts. The back of the tomb-
stone bears the following inscription which was added
much later: "Deborah Sampson Gannett, Robert Shurt-
leff, The Female Soldier, Service 1781–1783."

"Deborah, stop this morbid talk. I must go now, but I'll be back in a day or two. Mr. Cushman doesn't like me to go away every day."

Deborah stood by the window and watched Sylvia's carriage out of sight. Poor Sylvia, she led a stodgy life. The April day lay bonny on the farm. She remembered the April day over sixty years ago when Nehemiah was born and how afraid she had been of being put on the shelf.

Hannah, Jonny, Elisha, and Eph were all dead now. So were Jenny and Deacon and Mistress Thomas. She sat down in her chair by the window to watch for Benjamin and the grandson who would be driving the cows back to the barn from the pasture.

They found her there later in her chair—facing the window with a smile on her face.

April 29, 1827: Died at her home in Sharon, Massachusetts, Deborah Sampson Gannett, aged sixty-six years, four months, and ten days, beloved wife of Benjamin Gannett. Mrs. Gannett was the only known female soldier of the American Revolutionary War.

Afterword

Several years ago, while reading about the American Revolution, I came across a reference to Deborah Sampson, a Massachusetts girl who, it was said, had dressed up in men's clothes and enlisted and fought in the war. I could hardly believe this, but I decided to check on it at the Redwood Library in Newport, Rhode Island, where we were living at the time.

I was rewarded by finding among the rare books a

fictionalized memoir of the girl. It was a century-old republication of a still older book about Deborah. A Boston minister, John Adams Vinton, had in 1866 republished and made copious notes on THE FEMALE REVIEW by Herman Mann, a book published in 1797 during Deborah's lifetime.

The memoir itself was a puzzle to read because it was so full of contradictions and obvious historical errors, and the style was nauseatingly moralistic and affected. Nevertheless, it included an appealing account of her childhood, and places, people, and events were listed so that is was possible to sift the truth from it. Besides, Mr. Vinton's notes were readable and sensible.

At the Newport Historical Society Library, I began a systematic search of early American historical writings to see if she had caused any stir in her lifetime. I found little new about Deborah herself, but the period of her life-span intrigued me. Born in 1760, just as the Colonial troubles with Parliament were beginning to simmer, Deborah lived until 1827, when the United States was an established nation. She would have had firsthand news of the Boston Massacre, the Boston Tea Party, the Battle of Lexington, the signing of the Declaration of Independence.

Among some old newspaper files, I was jubilant to find a reference to her lecture tour. Lecture tour? What a bizarre thing for a woman to have done in those days.

In the meantime, I had written to the National Archives in Washington and found that Deborah had a service record, that she had served under the name Robert Shirtliff, had been pensioned, and that Congress had by Special Act voted a pension for her husband after her death. She was sufficiently famous that a Liberty ship had been named for her in World War II.

Furthermore, the Library of Congress had in its rare-book section the original 1797 FEMALE REVIEW.

The Daughters of the American Revolution Library allowed me to use its genealogical files to find out about Deborah's family. Her lineage was distinguished with Mayflower signers and famous early colonists including Miles Standish, John Alden, Peter Hobart, Abraham Sampson, and William Bradford.

The first task was to clear up the matter of how long she served. Herman Mann said she had been at the Battle of Yorktown and witnessed Cornwallis' surrender, although it appeared from other sources that she was living in Middleborough at that time.

This detail had greatly disturbed John Adams Vinton, as he brought out in his notes. My irrevocable conclusion was that her period of service was slightly less than two years and not the three years claimed by Mann, repeated by many later writers, and finally put in bronze and marble on various memorials.

Her earliest petition for pay, her enlistment certificate, and the church record all stated the later enlistment. I had also discovered from old history books that a "Continental Soldier" was one who enlisted for "the duration of the War or three years." Deborah had enlisted under those terms, pledging herself for three years, but not actually serving them, as the Army disbanded near the end of her second year of service.

Another question that troubled me was how she had managed to survive as a woman in the Army? There was no indication in all the myths and tales I found about her that her sex was ever suspected until discovered by the tactful Doctor Binney. Old books about the Army gave the answer. The soldiers never undressed. And with the casual way that they foraged for their own food and slept where they could find shelter, Deborah was able to attend to her personal sanitary needs by slipping off to the woods.

Also, why had Deborah allowed Herman Mann to put so many untruths into her memoirs? Clearly Herman Mann was writing a fictionalized book to sell. He had promised the subscribers, patrons who underwrote the cost of publication by paying for advance copies, that it would be an exciting book. He lifted whole passages from Thacher's MILITARY HISTORY describing the Battle of Yorktown and incorporated them in the book.

Perhaps Deborah never saw the manuscript before it was printed. In any case, she was not very pleased with it, for she asked him to revise it with the promise that he would take out the errors and republish it after her death. He rewrote it, still holding onto the Yorktown fiction, but it never appeared in print. This unpublished manuscript is at the Dedham, Massachusetts Historical Society.

This is a true story. All the names, places, people,

and events are correct insofar as I could possibly determine. The only two fictitious characters in the book are Zillah and Ike. There had to be an adult helper at Madam Thacher's, and it is a matter of record that Deborah's mother took her away because the work was too hard for the child, which certainly reflected on Zillah's character. Ike is just a name I picked for the kind of Army friend Deborah might have had.

I had the correct names and order, but not the dates of all the members of Deborah's immediate family, so I had to calculate the birth dates of several of them. Grand-mère's death date was a guess. I chose Uncle Nehemiah as the brother who took care of Deborah's mother and the smaller children. The memoir only says that they went to members of the family, and as there was an Uncle Nehemiah, that was a good guess.

Another guess was that the Reverend Sylvanus Conant chose GULLIVER'S TRAVELS as the book with which he rewarded Deborah. He was very kind to Deborah, and I hope he didn't give her a book of sermons for learning the Cathechism.

I also had to make a conjecture on how she spent the month of April, from the time she ran away from New Bedford until she enlisted at Bellingham. She would have had to work, and Boston would have been the best place to get lost.

The latter part of the FEMALE REVIEW contained a long and patently untruthful account of romantic ventures, fights with Indians, a trip to Ohio, and so on. I, along with Mr. Vinton, dismissed these as bad fiction, preferring to give Deborah an honest biography with facts that can be backed with her service record and official documents.

After her death, her heirs applied for a pension for Benjamin, who was old and ill. The papers carried many affidavits from neighbors as to the excellence of Deborah's character and intellect. The pension was granted, but it came after Benjamin's death. In the file is a tribute to Deborah that bears reprinting, an extract from a letter written ten years after Deborah's death by William Ellis, a U.S. Senator from Massachusetts:

February 4, 1837

"From my own acquaintance with Deborah Gannett, I can truly say she was a woman of uncommon native intellect and force of character. It happens that I have several connections who reside in the immediate neighborhood where Mrs. Gannett lived and died; and I have never heard from them, or any other source, any suggestions against the character of this heroine. Her stature was erect, and a little taller than the average height of females. Her countenance and voice were feminine; but she conversed with such ease on the subject of theology, on political subjects, and military tactics, that her manner would seem to be masculine. I recollect that once it occurred to my mind that her manner of conversation on any subject embraced that kind of demonstrative, illustrative style which we admire in the able diplomatist."

Cora Cheney

Bibliography

BOOKS

Abbot, Edward. Revolutionary Times. Boston, 1876.

Adams, Randolph G. New Light on the Boston Massacre. Worcester, 1938. (Publication of the American Antiquarian Society.)

Arnold, Samuel Greene. History of the State of Rhode Island and Providence Plantations. Vol. 2. New York, 1860.

Backus, Isaac. A History of New England With Particular Reference To the Baptists. 2 vols. Boston, 1777–1784.

Bowen, Catherine Drinker. John Adams and the American Revolution. Boston, 1950.

Bowen, Francis. A History of the United States of America. Boston, 1855.

Davis, William T. A History of Plimpton. From a History of Plymouth County, Massachusetts, compiled by D. Hamilton Hurd, Philadelphia, 1884.

Davis, William T. Ancient Landmarks of Plymouth. Boston, 1899.

Ellet, Mrs. Elizabeth F. Domestic History of the American Revolution. New York, 1850.

Ellet, Mrs. Elizabeth F. Women of the American Revolution.

Forbes, Esther. Paul Revere and the World He Lived In. Boston, 1942.

Ford, Paul Leicester. The New England Primer. New York, 1897.

Gannett, Mrs. Deborah. An Address, Delivered With Applause. (*Sic*) Dedham, 1802.

Gleeson, Alice Collins. Colonial Rhode Island. Pawtucket, 1926.

Grimshaw, William. A History of the United States. Philadelphia, 1820.

Hall, Ruth Gardiner. Descendants of Governor William Bradford. Compiled under the auspices of the Bradford Family Contract.

Headley, J. T. Washington and His Generals. New York, 1853.

Holbrook, Stewart. Lost Men of American History. New York, 1947.

Hovey, Alvah. The Life and Times of Isaac Backus. Boston, 1859.

Hurd, D. Hamilton. A History of Plymouth County, Massachusetts. Philadelphia, 1884.

Lossing, Benson J. Field Book of the American Revolution. New York, 1851–1852.

Mann, Herman. The Female Review or Memoirs of an American Young Lady. Dedham, 1797.

Martin, Joseph Plumb. Private Yankee Doodle. Edited by George F. Scheer. Boston, 1962.

Pease, Zephaniah. History of New Bedford. Boston, 1918.

Pierce, Ebeneazer W. History of Middleborough. From The History of Plymouth County, Massachusetts. Philadelphia, 1884.

Ramsay, David. A History of the American Revolution. Trenton, 1811.

Sampson, Gordon G. Our New England Sampsons. Privately Published. Lake George, New York, 1953.

Sanderson, John. Biographies of the Signers of the Declaration of Independence. Philadelphia, 1823.

Sheide, John H. The Lexington Alarm. Worcester, 1941. (Publication of the American Antiquarian Society.)

Shyrock, Richard H. Eighteenth Century Medicine in America. Worcester, 1950. (Publication of the American Antiquarian Society.)

Street, James. The Revolutionary War. New York, 1954.

Thacher, Dr. James. The American Revolution. New York, 1860.

Vinton, John Adams. The Giles Memorial. Boston, 1864.

Vinton, John Adams. Memoirs of the Sampson Family in America. Boston, 1864.

Vinton, John Adams. The Female Review, Edited With Notes. Boston, 1866.

Warwick, Pitz, and Wyckoff. Early American Dress. New York, 1965.

Weston, Thomas. The History of the Town of Middleborough. New York, 1906.

Wright, Richardson. Forgotten Ladies. Philadelphia, 1928.

MANUSCRIPT SOURCES

Record of the First Baptist Church of Middleborough (entry September 3, 1782).

Documents of the Commonwealth of Massachusetts concerning Deborah's back pay in 1792 consisting of Deborah's petition, a statement by Colonel Henry Jackson, and the muster certificate of Eliphalet Thorpe.

THE DIARY OF DEBORAH SAMPSON GANNETT IN 1802, a facsimile, hand copied and certified by Eugene Tappan of Sharon, Mass., July 11, 1901.

Family records of the Thomas and Sampson families.

Ten handwritten copybooks containing the unpublished, revised, 1827 manuscript memoir of Deborah, by Herman Mann. It was to have been published after her death and called "The Female Heroine or Memoirs of Miss Deborah Sampson." Also an unpublished 1850 version of the same material prepared by the son of Herman Mann, to be called "The American Heroine or Three Years Service With the Continental Army."

The service file and pension papers of Robert Shirtliff/Deborah Sampson, Rev. Soldier 32722, on file at the National Archives in Washington.

Plympton Vital Records. Book 2, page 718.

Paul Revere's letter concerning Deborah.

Service file and pension papers of Ephraim Sampson, Mass. W 11053, National Archives, for addenda on family history.

PICTURES

The only known portrait of Deborah is at the John Brown House, Rhode Island Historical Society, in Providence.

The Dedham Historical Society has a copper engraving of the portrait.

MISCELLANEOUS SOURCES

Massachusetts Soldiers and Sailors in the War of the Revolution. A compilation for the archives, published by the Secretary of the Commonwealth, Boston, 1896.

New England Genealogical and Antiquarian Register, page 276.

Allen's Biographical Dictionary, third edition.

Appleton's Cyclopaedia of American Biography. Vol. 5, page 382.

The Assembly's Catechism with notes of The Shorter Catechism of the Assembly of Divines at Westminster, by I. Watts.

Milk for Babes, Drawn Out of the Breasts of Both Testaments Chiefly for the Spiritual Nourishment of Boston Babes, by John Cotton

NEWSPAPERS AND MAGAZINES

New York Independent Gazette, Jan. 10, 1784.

The Massachusetts Spy, Jan. 26, 1792.

The Columbian Centinal and Massachusetts Federalist, March 20, 24, 27, 1802.

The Massachusetts Spy, July 21, 1802.

The Hampshire Gazette, Sept. 1, 1802.

The Village Register, Dedham, Dec. 29, 1820.

The Niles Register, Vol. XXXII, page 217, May 26, 1827.

The Nemosket Gazette, Middleborough, Mass. Sept. 1 (and ff. issues), 1857.

The Newport Mercury, Sept. 7, 1867, article by Thomas Wyatt.

The National Geographic, August, 1962—"Old Boston Post Roads," by Donald Barr Chidsey.

The New Yorker, July 3, 1937. "Revolutionary Heroine, Private Deborah Sampson," by Morris Bishop.

The D A R Magazine, 1917. Vol. 51, pages 140–222. "Three American Women Pensioned for Military Service," by Grace M. Pierce.